To my namesake
Perra Dee Knight

who is Now the Right
Age To begin the
learning of All the
things she must Know
To Stay Always As
Charming, Poised And
beautiful As She is
Today on her 11th
birthday —
Stay Sweet!
Aunt Dee

The Hairdo Handbook

THE HAIRDO HANDBOOK

A COMPLETE GUIDE TO HAIR BEAUTY

Dorothea Zack Hanle

Editor, HairDo Magazine

DOUBLEDAY & COMPANY, INC., GARDEN CITY, NEW YORK
1964

Library of Congress Catalog Card Number 64-11744
Copyright © 1964 by Dell Publishing Co., Inc.
Printed in the United States of America
First Edition

Contents

Contents

The Hairdo Handbook

CHAPTER I

The Importance of a Hairdo

How important is a hairdo? Far more than most of us would care to admit. Really beautiful hair artfully arranged has a magic capable of redeeming the plainest of faces, even mesmerizing us into thinking the most impossible jumble of features is attractive. A pretty new coif can send your spirits soaring, just as a dreary one can depress you. And unlike any other fashion or beauty accessory—for that is what your hair really is—a hairdo can truly express your individuality. The nice part of that, too, is the fact that no matter your income or station in life, you can have a custom-made coif that's uniquely yours, distinctly you.

Time was when a woman felt the need of a lift—mentally, physically or psychologically, and she would impulsively buy a new hat. She felt younger, gayer, looked suddenly prettier —but the effect was temporary. Today, for more lasting results, a change of hairstyle—yes, a change of color, too, perhaps—turns the trick, has you floating on air. For, let's face it, there's truly nothing more emotionally uplifting to a woman's spirits than the admiration in a man's eyes. More often than not, a man's head is turned by lovely hair.

Beautiful hair is possible for every woman, young or old— so very easily possible that there is no excuse for your not having hair that frames your face with glowing color, touch-me texture, and loveliness of line and arrangement. You may achieve this yourself—and the world of highly developed hair cosmetics offers you a tempting array of delightful aids. But you will probably be happiest, most confident of success and assured of perfect-for-you styling if you *first* enlist the help of a well-trained professional. He or she can guide you to the most appropriate and attractive hairdo for you, can advise you on the basic care for your particular kind of hair. After that, should budget or time dictate that you "do-it-yourself," you'll find the pages of this book invaluable. If you're a teen exploring the possibilities of hairstyling, you'll find a world of ideas to try in these pages. And, if you're a busy wife and mother whose time is stretched many ways, you will want to use this as a handbook to keep you looking up-to-date, to show you ways to make your own and your children's hair more attractive. There's even a tip or two for husbands and their special hair problems.

Business girls and career women know the special value of looking their best—often the decisive factor in securing a position and achieving success. This book is for you, too, and for grandmothers and great-grandmothers. In fact, it's for everyone who yearns for beautiful hair and a beautiful hairdo and is designed to help you achieve exactly that.

CHAPTER II

Getting to Know Your Own Hair

It's fun to choose a hairdo. But before you start shopping for your style, you'd better know the material with which you (or your hairdresser) have to work. Begin by analyzing your hair—study it closely, carefully, critically. How does it grow? Is it healthy? What is the texture? The color? What are its assets and its liabilities or problems? Before you can find out what to do with your hair, how to arrange it, how to have it styled, cut, tinted, or waved (or straightened, as the case may be), you'll have to *know* your hair. And whether you plan to take your head in your own hands—or to a professional—you'll save time, avoid errors if you first do a little studying of your hair.

How does it grow? For the average person, hair grows at the rate of about one half inch per month. And the average woman has approximately 150,000 hairs on her head. The average age of a single hair is from two to five years. No two hairs are alike ever in intensity of color. Only two basic pigments are found in hair—brown and red—and it is the combination in varying degrees of these pigments which causes the great variety of hair colors in the world. The only truly black hair is said to be that of the Chinese, and the dark hair of Indians (American and Far Eastern) is not black but has such an intensity of red pigment that it looks black. About 12 per cent of our population has naturally red hair. And natural blondes, whose coloring is also in the minority, have more hairs per head than those with darker shades. So much for the general facts about hair. Now, what about *your* hair?

You inherited certain basic characteristics of your tresses. For the laws of heredity determined precisely whether your hair will be straight or curly, light or dark, or something in between. Some characteristics of your hair are very special and distinct and are based on inheritance of individual features; these include cowlicks, hairline shape, baldness, and others. But the color of your hair and its straight or wavy or curly character are subject to the rules of what biologists call "recession" and "dominance." Here's how that works: For each dominant-recessive trait, you receive two "genes" —the tiny messengers of heredity—one from each parent. If they are different, the dominant one will show; the recessive one will not be apparent in your appearance—but it may still influence the appearance of your children. Each child you have will get from you just one of the two kinds of genes you carry for that particular trait, and he or she will receive one from your husband. Whether you pass on the dominant or the recessive gene to your child is a matter of chance.

Now the rule for hair color is this: darker hair is always dominant. Similarly, curliness is dominant to straightness. Of course, there are many shadings of hair and there are many degrees of curliness or straightness. Red hair genes are rare and will only appear as real red when combined with pure blonde genes; otherwise, they appear as warm tones in darker hair. Recessive traits are always for hair straighter or lighter than one's own, so that your child's hair can be only as dark as that of the darker-haired parent. Similarly, it will be no curlier than that of the curlier-haired parent.

Now let's examine how your inheritance really grows. Each hair emerges from a small cavity or depression on the scalp called a follicle. It's a saclike bag at the base of the hair strand. If the follicle is straight, a straight shaft of hair emerges. If the follicle is curled or wavy, so grows the hair shaft. Incidentally, you can stop raising your eyebrows when your straight-haired friend speaks wistfully of her baby curls. It's possible. In growing, her scalp expanded and the curved follicles that produced those first baby curls may have straightened out. The same sort of change can take place in adults, too, when some factor—an illness or high fever, perhaps—has caused the scalp to expand. Then later, as the scalp contracts, the shape of the follicles may be altered and with it, the shape and direction of the hair growing from them. You can have temporary changes, when a sudden fright or shock or a terrifying dream, for example, causes the tiny muscles around your follicles to contract; your hair "stands on end." That's how active and sensitive your follicles are.

Your hair itself has no blood supply or nerves, but a network of blood vessels surrounds each follicle and nourishes the hair root in the follicle. When you are worried and tense, the nerves around the blood vessels contract, cutting off the supply of blood. Similarly, nerves that are injured or diseased affect the blood supply and consequently the health of the hair. Bear in mind that even though the hair itself does not have nerves or blood cells, it does grow. Lubricating and promoting the gloss and sheen of your hair are the little oil glands that open into the follicle onto the emerging, ever growing hair shaft. From time to time certain follicles become temporarily inactive and stop producing hair. This is usually nature's way of providing time out for a very busy follicle, and in due course, it will resume its function. Beware, however, of the follicle that has gone on a sit-down strike for other reasons—excessive heat, infection, or too many conflicting reactions that have irritated the scalp. Those are the follicles that need special attention to revive them, lest they become permanently damaged and never produce hair again.

The hair shaft is in three layers: The innermost one (the *medulla*) is made of large, loosely connected cells, roundish in shape, containing keratin—an albuminous substance also found in feathers, horns, and hoofs. It is these cells, with air spaces between them influencing the reflection of light, that account for the sheen and tone of your hair. The middle layer (the *cortex*) has spindle-shaped, keratinized cells locked or cemented together. These contain melanin, which determines your hair color. The outer, protective layer (the *cuticle*) has tight, overlapping cells, which are colorless and translucent.

As each hair shaft emerges from its follicle, it is, for the most part, in good condition. Damage occurs from exposure —to sun, the elements, salt water, chlorinated water, abusive handling, the use of inferior products, or the misuse of reputable products (see Problem Hair, Chapter XII). Examine a single hair from your head. First, study texture: Coarse hair feels rough, is often wiry, frequently hard to manage. Fine hair is silky, soft, often lacks body, and can normally be limp, lacking elasticity. It lacks, in some cases, the inner layer (medulla) of the hair shaft—also lacking in the downy fuzz (called lanugo hair) on many new babies' heads. Next, check your hair for porosity—or its ability to absorb moisture. Lack of porosity and overporosity are problems. Wet your hair and notice how quickly it gets soaking wet. Instantly—it's overporous; if a great deal of water is needed—it's nonporous. Overporous hair results, usually, from damage by overbleaching, overexposure to alien elements (see Chapter XII). It will be harsh, brittle, dull.

Now test your hair shaft for elasticity: Pull the strand you've removed, holding it at either end, and slowly stretch it until it snaps. You should be able to stretch it about one fifth more of its length, and when it snaps, if elasticity is good (i.e., normal), the ends will curl.

Healthy hair, beautiful hair begins right at the follicles, which are nourished by the blood stream. If there's something faulty about the nourishment the follicles get from the blood—something missing or a lack of balance in the diet— it's going to show in your hair.

Scientific experiments have shown that a lack of fatty acids in the diet can make hair dry and lusterless—that just the addition of some form of oil to the diet is enough, in some cases, to turn the trick and add life to the hair. Similarly, a lack of vitamin A—the yellow-vegetable vitamin—can show up in the hair, weakening it, causing dry, flaky scalp. And research has shown the vitamin B family to be closely related to hair health—to color and to growth. Not enough is yet known to say for sure how much it can do, but experiments with inositol, a B vitamin (sources: blackstrap molasses, any of the B-complex foods), in treatment of certain kinds of baldness have shown some success.

All this doesn't mean that you should settle down to a menu of salad oil, carrots, and blackstrap molasses three times a day. Actually, a balanced diet, one that has enough from each of the main food groups, should give you these important hair-beauty essentials. Your daily diet should include food from *each* of these categories: the milk group; the high-protein group (two or more servings a day), including meat, fish, eggs, poultry, dry beans, peas, nuts; the vegetable-fruit group (four or more servings a day, including a dark green and yellow vegetable and a citrus fruit); bread-cereal group (four or more servings daily). The other foods—fats, oils, sugars—that you need are usually included in adequate quantity in cooking or serving these. And if you're weight-cutting, *don't* cut out a group. Eat less from each, and let your doctor guide you.

Now you know about the background of your hair—what makes it grow, why it's healthy or unhealthy, where its color and tendency to curl or not come from. Next step: Inspect it more closely, note its present special condition and quality, and analyze what you've been doing to it. If you're in search of a new hairdo, a new hair color, perhaps a whole new change of hair character (waving, straightening, a radical cut, for instance), then a check list of the present state of your hair can be of value. Not only is such an evaluation important to you in assessing the pluses and minuses of your hair, but, if you plan to try a new hairdresser, your analysis can save his and your time in evolving your new coif.

In the chart below, simply check the items that now apply to you and fill in the blanks where indicated. Then you can make a copy of the results to take to your hair stylist, or, if you're hairdoing at home, consult the index for where to find solutions to any special problems that appear in your self-hair-analysis.

HAIRDO ANALYSIS CHART

HAIR TEXTURE:	HAIR MASS:
——Coarse	——Thick and bushy
——Medium	——Thick and man-ageable
—✗—Fine	—✗—Average
——Baby-fine and wispy	——Thin
	——Very thin-to-balding

DEGREE OF CURL:

———Straight, no body
———Straight, with body
——X Slight wave
———Wavy
———Curly
———Too curly, wiry

HAIR CONDITION:

—X Normal, healthy
———Excessively oily
—X Oily
———Dry, dull
———Dry, brittle, split
———Overbleached
         with breakage

SCALP CONDITION:

———Normal, healthy
———Excessively oily
X Oily
———Dry, tight, itchy
———Dry, flaky
———Dandruff

HAIRLINE:

———No problems
———Too-low brow
—X Too-high brow
———Too-low nape
———Receding
———Irregular

HAIR COLOR:

—X Natural, never artificially colored
———Natural, previously tinted permanently
———Natural, previously tinted with temporary color
———Natural, previously tinted semipermanently
—X Colored with permanent color
———Colored with temporary color
———Colored with semipermanent color

State original natural color of hair:——brown——————
If hair is colored with permanent tint, how often do you have
     this done? Whole head————; Retouching————.
If hair is colored with semipermanent color, how often:——
If hair is tipped, streaked or frosted, how often:————————

PERMANENT WAVES:

——Whole permanent
——Partial or area permanent
——Body or underpermanent
——Soft-wave permanent
——Permanent for curl
——Hair straightening

CURLABILITY:

—X—Hard to wave
——Easy to wave
——Average

HAIR POROSITY:

——Normal
——Overporous
——Nonporous

ELASTICITY:

—X—Normal
——Poor
——Very poor

PRODUCTS USED: (At home or in the salon and specify brands for your hairdresser)

Shampoo: RK men 8yr
Cream rinse:
Setting lotion:
Hair spray:
Temporary color:

Semipermanent color:
Permanent color:
Conditioners:
Permanent wave:
Other:

SPECIAL PROBLEMS:

Cowlicks (and where): Pront right
Hard-to-curl areas (and where): Front
Eyeglasses (show them to the hairdresser):
Slow growth rate:
Fast growth rate:
Other:

SPECIAL DATES:

Last permanent: Last coloring job:
Last hair straightening: Last shampoo:
Last conditioning treatment: Last trim:
Last haircut: *Vets Day*
Your birthday: *Jan 3*
   (Yes, your age and hor-
    monal changes have an
    effect on your hair's be-
    havior)

AND ABOUT YOU:

State your occupation and/or special activities:
Do you wear a hat: ——most of the time;
   ——some of the time; ——never
What is your favorite hobby or sport:
Do you wish to look: ——older; ——younger; ——your age

What kinds of hairstyles do you like:

——formal	——very short	——updos
——casual	——medium	——smooth dos
——classic	X long	——wavy dos
——short	X very long	——curly dos
	——two-or-three-way dos	
	——the current rage	
	——a variety	

Do you enjoy doing your own:
——setting   ——permanenting
——coloring   ——conditioning
X shampooing
Are you reasonably skillful at putting up your hair:
——yes ——no

Armed with the results gleaned from your hairdo analysis, you're now ready to go in search of the perfect hairdo for you. If you'd do it yourself, then read the next chapter for some further self-analysis and for how to choose what's really right for you. If you plan to let a hairdresser make the decision for you, then read Chapter IV on how to find a good stylist, one who's best for your hair, your budget, your busy life, and your special taste and activities.

CHAPTER III

How to Find a Style

What shows is *style*. After you've established the health of your hair, good health, that is, you're ready for an attractive and becoming hairdo. The choice is limitless today, but the problem is: Which is for you? Which one not only looks well on you but makes you *feel* wonderful wearing it?

There are so many factors to consider when making your selection. Your face shape, your special arrangement of features, the proportions and size of your figure, the life you lead and your activities, the time and money you have to spend—all these should be appraised. Then there are the special, individual problems—of noses, eyes, eyeglasses, the nature of the hair. Too bad there isn't some magical instant way like saying, "Abracadabra, that's the hairdo for me," and have it settle on your head just like that. (Of course, a wig might be the answer—but that, too, must be styled with all those factors taken into account!)

Artists, photographers, beauty experts—all proclaim the oval as the perfect face shape. And, 'tis said, she who has an oval face can wear any hairstyle. Well, that would be true enough if you could select a hairdo with just your face as the criterion. That's important enough all right, but there's the rest of you to consider too. So, before you choose, study yourself in a full-length mirror, as if you were a stranger.

More than shape, size, or problem features, there is another aspect of you. What is your *total* look? Are you a "type?"

When you accidentally catch your reflection in a mirror—and you have that fleeting feeling of having seen someone else (or yourself as others see you)—what do you see? Are you a well-scrubbed, all-American outdoor type? Then bypass the siren hairdos and sensational colors if you would be your prettiest self. Is yours a sparkling-eyed, dark-haired, Irish colleen look? With a hint or more of natural curl? Then don't try for an ash-blonde pure-line Swedish coif. Is it a petite, pixie, or gamin face? No exotic hairdos for you either. Have you a regal or madonna look? Then detour the feather- and ruffle-cuts. Be yourself. Be your type.

What about your figure? Tall, short, slim, or stout—which are you? Have you considered the whole length and breadth of you in relation to your hairdo? Better step up to a three-way mirror and get the total picture. The trick is to know your proportions, learn the artist's dodges of illusion to camouflage the less than ideal, and to develop a sense of scale. Although this sounds like a large order and you may say, "But I'm not an artist"—we say it's really very simple. Each of us has a little of the artist in us or we wouldn't care about a pretty hairdo in the first place. Here's the way to study your figure—and what you can do about your hairdo in relationship to it. If you are too short, don't, above all, have an inferiority complex about it—hold yourself "tall" and think "tall" (and remember that men most often like "little women"). Avoid wearing your hair too long, too fluffy, too elaborately styled. Try on an overlarge hat and see how disproportionate it is for you. The same holds for an oversize hairdo. Avoid too tall coifs, too—they can add actual inches, but make the rest of you look like a midget. Wear a "little head" look, one of the pretty bobs that are never out of fashion and that can be varied with many details of styling. If, in addition, you are also too fat (you should diet it off, you know) or of a stocky, chunky build, the same rule applies. But you will then wear a medium-length do—not one that's so brief it will make your figure look even pudgier.

Too tall—and skinny too? In a world of high-fashion-conscious women, this is no longer a handicap. But do wear your hair long enough to avoid a too-tiny-head-for-the-body look. If you're very tall and also very full-figured—or even fat—don't try fussy hairdos. Stick to the simple, the classic, off-the-neck in back, wide-waved, well-groomed coif. No curls for you. If you're hippy, you'll find that a hairdo with some width will help to bring your figure into an illusion of symmetry. And, happy you, if you're average, you can concentrate on other features or faults, as the case may be. Study your shoulders, for instance. Observe how your head sits upon them, how your hairdo relates to their proportions. Sloped and drooping shoulders (some are born of nature and some acquired through laziness) are only accentuated by long, relaxed, page-boy styles. Medium-length hair, softly styled and groomed is best. Too-narrow shoulders should not be umbrella-ed by a big, bouffant coif of extreme width but can be made to look broader with a small, cap-coif—a sleek one or a tossed-curl variety.

What about our necks? Too few of us are blessed with arching, gracefully swanlike throats and necks. But the illusion can be evoked for many with a suitable hairdo. The scrawny neck may be softened appreciably with a style that keeps the back hair longer than the natural hairline and filled out. This fashion is best, too, for the neck that is too long and not so gracefully arched. A short neck requires the reverse treatment of the long neck, and long back hair should be avoided. Short hairdos are fine, and a few medium-length styles will work nicely if the neck is not too squatty. Plump necks cannot take fussy-back hairdos, and severe upsweeps are never for those with untidy napes or hairlines that grow too low on the neck.

While much has been said and written about your face shape and its features with respect to your hairdo, little or nothing has been said about the importance of the shape and size of the head. The outlines of a man's head are more obvious, and we are much more aware of the various head shapes on men than on women. Yet, beneath those pretty and provocative coifs, there are many pointed, egg, flat, and even literally square heads. Lucky we are to be able to conceal some of nature's mistakes so beautifully.

Take the pointed or pixie head shape, for instance—with the high crown that actually comes to a peak at top. This is one of the most difficult head shapes to coif, and the hair stylists often tend to give these heads an exaggerated Queen Nefertiti hairdo. For extreme fashion for evening wear, this can be breath-takingly beautiful, but it is hardly practical or acceptable for everyday casual American living. One way to offset the "peak" is by using a low diagonal part in the hair, beginning low at the hairline and ascending to the peak. (For more about the wonderful things you can do with parts, see Chapter XVII.) For the head with an abrupt "shelf" at the nape—naturally, the upswept back is out. The better style is one which is medium length with soft, loose curls to cover the back.

The too-narrow head demands smoothness at the back and fluffy, soft waves or wings at the sides. The too-broad head needs fluffiness and fullness at the back, closeness at the sides —as does the head that's too flat in back. And for the short, round head shape, one of the most effective hairstyles is the irregular, layered cut (see Chapter XVII).

Ears and all their fanciful shapes are part of your head outline too. Jutting, flyaway, or extra-big ones exposed for all to see can ruin the illusion of an otherwise lovely hairdo. Best hide them under a curved, gently pouffed-at-sides coif.

You may have some other special problems—other than face shape (which we'll discuss later) and other than those already outlined as you study your total image. Here are some common ones, with suggested ways to camouflage or cover up and thus distract the observer's eye from a less-than-perfect feature:

Long nose: Balance and counteract with back masses of hair; never crowd the face with hair which can only serve to frame and emphasize the long nose.

Large nose: Balance it with large, curved waves; never emphasize with fussy hair details and tiny curls on small hairdos.

Short nose: Try a brief cap cut with short-short curls or a feather cut.

Too-full face: Wear a hairdo with height and sweep hair away from the widest and fullest part of the face.

Uneven hairline: Cover it with bangs or a bandeau of hair drawn diagonally across the forehead.

High forehead: Avoid skinned-back dos and ponytails and wear long, thick bangs or a bandeau of hair swooping low on the brow.

Bulging forehead: Try large, shallow waves brought forward to minimize the bulge.

Low forehead: Small, tidy hairdos with off-the-face lines heighten the look of the forehead. Or brief bangs, started an inch or two above the normal hairline can hide the fact.

Weak chin: This can be strengthened by fluffs of curls below the ears.

Double chin: Wear upswept hairstyles—and try to keep chin up too.

Jutting chin: Soften the look with medium-length hair,

never pulled back, but crowding the face. If short hair is desired, wear it brushed high and full at top, full at front.

Eyeglasses: Avoid long bangs or fluffy arrangements on the brow. Always wear hairdos that cover earpieces on eyeglass frames. Wear frames that leave eyebrows exposed. See further tips, Chapter XII.

Eyes too small, close: Wear hairdos that give width to the eye area of your face: those that are drawn back from temples, perhaps fastened at back crown with a French twist or swinging loose in a ponytail flip. Avoid long bangs, but if you must have them for some other facial fault, keep them short, fringy, wispy.

Perhaps you've none of these special problems (lucky you!), but your face shape is giving you trouble. If you suspect that's the stumbling block between you and an attractive, appropriate hairdo, try this: pull hair back from the face (or slip on a bathing cap that fits snugly and tuck all hair in) and study it in your mirror. Take a ruler and see how your face measures up to the artist's concept of the ideal oval: flat, horizontal measurements—5 inches across forehead, 5½ inches under eyes, 4½ inches under nose, 3¼ inches under lips. And from chin tip to hairline, 7½ inches. Didn't quite make it? Or way, way off? Then, perhaps you fit into one of these geometric categories:

Round: Nearly circular, with rounded apple cheeks, a full chin, perhaps a fairly low forehead.

Square: Jaw line is about as wide as the cheeks, and the forehead is squared off.

Oblong: A long face, roughly rectangular, with the jaw about as wide as forehead and cheeks.

Diamond: Width is concentrated at the middle, and both the forehead and the jaw are narrow.

Triangle: A wide chin and jaw, tapering up from cheeks to a narrow forehead.

Inverted triangle: Brow is very broad, jaw area narrow, chin sometimes pointed.

Those are the basic, pure shapes. You're rare if you have a perfectly round or perfectly square face—or perfectly any of the other shapes. But if your study of your face comes close to one of these, here are some suggestions for achieving that desirable oval face illusion with your hair:

Round: Do use an asymmetrical line to help de-emphasize the roundness—a side part, a dip or pouf on one side. Keep hair full and soft above the ears so that the illusion of height or elongation is given to the round shape. *Don't* part hair in the middle, flatten it on top, or have fussy little round curls that create circular effects and thereby emphasize the roundness of your face shape.

Square: Do place emphasis on the top, to soften the square lines, add height, detract from the too-broad jaw. Use curvy bangs, diagonal parts, or soft, full waves to achieve this effect. Soft fullness at the sides can help round out the shape with pleasing effects. *Don't* style hair too severely, pull it back at the temples, or have it too wide at the lower sides. Avoid severe details, curls, or waves that are too regular.

Oblong: Do choose a style with some fullness at the sides, to add more width there. Bangs are another help, especially if your forehead is very high—the horizontal line helps shorten the face length. A low side part can help as well; it shortens the brow, helps round out the corners if brow's squarish. *Don't* wear very high hairdos that add unwanted length to your face. And stay away from very sleek styles— you need more softness in your coif to round the angles.

Diamond: Do keep hair full and wide at the top (but not too high) to broaden the brow, de-emphasize the wide cheek span. Keep hair soft at sides, and experiment with lengths to see which is most becoming—probably a little below ear length, with upturned ends, though a very short length might work if chin is not pointed. *Don't* brush hair straight back from ears and temples; that will make your face seem even more of a diamond. And avoid bangs that tend to narrow the brow.

Triangle: Do try for added width at the brow with a style that lifts hair at the temples, curves it around the brow in soft, wide arcs. Try an angular part, starting low near the temple and angling it up to crown. *Don't* wear full, winging lower sides that exaggerate jaw's width. And avoid straight, severe styles.

Inverted Triangle: Do enlist fluffy, asymmetrical bangs that cover part—not all—of the brow, to narrow, not broaden, it. Or try a little fullness at the jaw area to make it appear wider, less pointed. A diagonal, off-center part also can help. *Don't* adopt middle parts, straight-across bangs, or behind-the-ear hairdos.

Perhaps none of these specifics has helped you at all. Then it's trial-and-error for you until you find what's becoming, comfortable, appropriate. But wait! There are some ways to experiment without sacrificing a lock of your own hair to trial-and-error, or a penny of your money, either. There are these try-on tricks which may give you a clue:

Shampoo-sculpture: Next hair-washing time, just whip up a dense lather of shampoo in your hair, and start "sculpting" a do or two or three in front of your mirror. Sounds like child's play, but you can actually get hairdo-line effects by moving your hair about, copying the lines of coifs you've admired in fashion hairdo photographs. Move the sudsed hair away from those areas where no fullness is necessary, pile it up, fill in places where you think there need be mass, use it as a camouflage to cover, or distract attention from, less-than-perfect features. Try upsweeps, bangs, diagonal bandeaux across the forehead, swirled waves, piled curls, a head-hugging cap.

Mirror-painting: Take an old lipstick (or a cake of soap) and outline your face on the mirror as you look into it. Then try outlining various hair silhouettes around that face shape. Have someone else outline your profile and then draw side views of dos too.

Picture-play: Have a series of inexpensive snapshots taken from front, side, back (or better yet, do this at an automatic, self-service picture-taking machine if there's one in your vicinity), again with hair drawn tightly back or encased in a plain bathing cap, so that no hair is visible—just face and head shape. Next, cut out the pictures, carefully trimming off everything but you. Tape these silhouettes on plain paper and start drawing hairdos you'd like to wear around them. Study the effects. If you like none, pick up your pictures and tape them to a fresh piece of paper and continue to draw hair outlines until you find one or more you think looks well.

Wig-try: If you really feel that you can't trust your own judgment or artistry in the foregoing experiments, then go to your hairdresser or a shop where wigs are sold. Try on one or more in different styles (and colors too). That way you'll see instantly what's becoming and what isn't. Hairpieces, half wigs, chignons—try-ons of these can give you some effective judging aids too.

In your search for that ultimate coif for you, beware of one trap: Don't copy someone else's hairdo just because you admire that person and her way of wearing her tresses. To be copied is the highest form of flattery. To copy is to be a sheep. In the world of fashion, unless you design and make, or have made, your own clothes, it's almost impossible to avoid meeting your new dress on someone else. But a hairdo is another matter. Your hair is one accessory that can be custom-made for you and you alone. Even if you do admire a glamorous celebrity's coif, you shouldn't attempt to have a hair-for-hair copy on your own head. Even if you were Jacqueline Kennedy's identical twin, her hairdo could be wrong for you simply because your way of life is different from hers. You should choose your hairdo not only because it's right for your face shape, for the total look of you, but for how and where you live and who you are.

As you turn the pages of fashion magazines you will see coifs that will be copied over and over, as though cooky-cuttered out on an assembly line. Don't be tempted to follow the leader. That's a children's game and you're a grownup. You would, and should, be you, no matter the prevailing winds of fashion. If it's blowing bubble coifs or stirring up a storm of bouffants and these styles aren't becoming to your hair and you, turn your back on the breeze till it blows over. You can be sure that the fashion will change as inevitably as the season, and the next may be more suited to you. Even then, it should be *adapted* to you—not copied exactly. A good stylist will adapt the coif of your choice by altering a wave direction, or adding a curl or modifying a bang that's too long or too wispy for you, so that your smart, current coif will evolve as one distinctly, individually your own.

Remember that the hairdo news and styles you read and see should serve only as a guide to be used as they meet your needs and taste. You do not buy a ready-made hairdo as you would a dress or hat. (And even a wig must be so treated— as if it were your very own hair.) That's the beauty of this, your most exciting fashion accessory—it's custom-designed for you. And it's almost the last one where a woman, no matter her status, can truly express her individuality—and her femininity. So don't throw away your opportunity—don't have a cooky-cutter hairdo. Be yourself!

CHAPTER IV

How to Find the
Best Hairdresser for You

Even the born do-it-yourselfer must ultimately seek the services of a hairdresser. For the real heart of a lovely hairdo is the haircut, which *must* be handled by a true professional. You may shampoo, set, permanent, or color-rinse your locks to your heart's content without getting into serious trouble. But cutting, shaping, styling—that's for the trained expert. If you want a permanent color change, you'll need professional help for that too (see Chapter X). Even the woman who wears her hair long should consult a hairdresser periodically (see Chapter XVIII), for her problems are very special ones.

Finding a good hairdresser—one whose services and prices are right for you—is not the easiest trick. Whether you live in the city or Smalltown, U.S.A., you'll have to spend a few trial-and-error appointments and do some research before discovering the best salon for your hair, your taste, and your pocketbook. Here, then, are a few suggestions to help you reach your goal as quickly as possible.

Check first with friends whose hairdos you most admire. Check with more than one, and when you find several who patronize the same salon, give it a try. Or write to the beauty-fashion editor of your home-town paper and ask her to recommend several salons. If the town or city is new to you, study the salon ads in the newspaper. Look for those that emphasize custom service, top quality, and fashion rather than gimmicks or special price reductions. Then, before making your appointment, make a few telephone calls to find out whether the cost of cut, shampoo, and set are within your budget.

How much does a hairdo cost? It can vary, depending on what you want and where you get it, as much as the price of a new hat. For a big-name hairdresser's attention to your coif, you may expect to pay as much more, proportionately, as you would for an original creation by a big-name milliner. Yet it is possible to get good workmanship in a reputable and much less expensive salon. The trick to this is knowing something of what you want before you start and knowing what's becoming to you.

On occasion, you may wish to patronize one of the higher-priced, "name" salons. But the best hairdo for you is not necessarily the most expensive you could buy. For a big spree in the big city you can expect to spend anywhere from $10 for a restyling, haircut, shampoo, and set (depending on length of hair) to $30 or more for a coloring job. There are specialty shops in New York City and many others where you can get the works on hair and makeup for $30 or more. These major dos or redos require the better part of a day, so wherever you go for your beauty spree, plan to spend time as well as money. The hairdresser is selling you his time with his skill and he must have your co-operation to give you his best.

Shopping around the country, you will note the cost of permanents and sets varying this way: In some parts of the Far West, average prices range higher than in some Eastern cities, including New York. In Los Angeles, Portland, San Francisco, and Seattle, the average for a permanent (including, of course, shampoo, trim, set) runs from $11 to $16.69

(in that order), as against a range of $8.20 to $11.50 (in that order) in Scranton, Pa., New York City, and Pittsburgh. Baltimore and Washington, D.C., run slightly higher. The most recent table from the United States Bureau of Labor Statistics giving average prices in major cities, for a cold wave, with shampoo, trim, but not a full haircut or restyling:

Atlanta	$11.75
Baltimore	12.13
Boston	10.62
Chicago	12.35
Cincinnati	8.63
Cleveland	11.55
Detroit	11.52
Houston	14.25
Kansas City	15.00
Los Angeles	11.00
Minneapolis	9.76
New York	10.24
Philadelphia	10.50
Pittsburgh	11.50
Portland	12.09
St. Louis	12.00
San Francisco	12.90
Scranton	8.20
Seattle	16.69
Washington, D.C.	13.28

For a shampoo and set, the average price (short hair) runs from a little over $1.00 in St. Louis to a little more than $2.00 in Kansas City. In New York City, add another dollar. It can't be that such variations depend entirely on quality of work; a number of other factors—local custom, competition, and economy—enter in. In some cities, a uniform price scale is agreed upon by local hairdressers. In others, prices vary widely from shop to shop, depending on location, décor, reputation, advertising, size and skill of staff.

In general, operators earn more where the traffic bears the highest tariff. Therefore, the most highly skilled tend to congregate in the most expensive shops. But there are plenty of exceptions to this; the independent operator, no matter how skillful, may prefer to run his own shop on neighborhood lines and at neighborhood rates. It's possible, then, for you to discover your dream hairdresser in an unlikely area. Just possible. And this will be your best buy, if you find one that does a good job for you.

What about tipping? This is a ticklish topic in any field where services are rendered and one on which Americans notoriously are apt to err—in either direction. If you're a timid soul, you may overtip; if you're too independent, you may get tagged as a tightwad whom nobody wishes to serve.

The happiest course is the middle ground, your best guide being a percentage of the total bill. If you patronize an assembly-line shop and try to give a quarter to every operator who touches your hair, this can mount up.

You are *not* expected to tip the proprietor or salon owner (or his wife), although, in some cases, his charge will be higher to include the would-be tip. Most operators' salaries are fixed in the expectation of supplemental tips. And, as may often happen, you will get a shampoo, set, manicure, and comb-out from three or four different operators. In such cases, it's wise to give the receptionist a percentage of the total to be divided among all who served you. If you expect to be a regular customer and get good service, you should tip as generously as you can. But it has to be played more or less by ear—the amount varying from 10 to 25 per cent. For example, in most salons, except the plush ones, you would pay $3.00 to $4.00 for a regular wash, trim (slight) and set, with 35 cents to $1.00 added for tips, depending on the number of operators who had a hand in your hairdo. Once you've tried out tipping, according to your own best judgment, you can tell better on subsequent visits how to hit a happy medium. Often, a friendly receptionist can be your best counsel on this score too.

From the most reasonable to the most expensive salons, the business of buying a new hairdo is a co-operative venture. The success of your new coif depends as much on you as on your hairdresser. When you find a good man or woman, know how to give him or her your attention, your time, your courtesy. Only then can you expect the best workmanship. Whether you think of your hairdresser as an artist, a professional person or a craftsman, his status as far as etiquette is concerned is similar to that of your dentist. You should accord him the courtesy of your best manners. Here, for example, is what should happen.

If you are contemplating a complete change-over and have had no previous dealings with the particular shop where the "revolution" is to take place, both you and the hairdresser would profit by a preliminary visit. If possible, make an appointment for a get-acquainted-with-my-problem visit—just a few minutes, at a time convenient to him. Then, first of all, do tell him that you plan to become his steady customer. Briefly outline your hair problems and pet peeves, such as exposed ears, hair shorn too short at the nape, or whatever else. Tell him your ideas about the kind of style you think you would like, and hear his ideas for you. If you are satisfied with his suggested style, agree to it, and later, when you go for your styling, don't fight it.

Schedule your appointment, and be sure to arrive promptly. Greet the receptionist or salon owner and tell her your name. She will show you the dressing room. Put on the smock provided for you (take off your blouse or dress, as you will be quite warm under the dryer), and after removing any bobby pins or hair ornaments, proceed to the shampooing station. "What kind of shampoo would you like?" you will be asked. If you have no preference, state whether your hair is dry, oily, or normal, tinted, or overbleached, and let the operator decide. Co-operate with her. If she asks you to sink back in the chair and tilt your head way back, do it. A professional shampoo is a joy to your hair, and the massage and stimulation is something you will not be able to duplicate exactly at home. Relax. Enjoy it without talking. When it is finished, go directly to the styling table or station indicated to you. Don't stop to chat with a friend, and don't pay a prolonged visit to the ladies' room. Your hair should be wet to be shaped and styled. If you have not had a preliminary visit with the stylist, outline briefly the style you would like to have and ask him if he agrees. He may have a better idea. Listen to him. Remember that a good stylist must shape your hair before he styles it. Asking him not to do so is like asking a sculptor not to moisten the clay. The style must have a line, and the line comes from the cut.

With the shaping done, the setting begins. Your help may be needed. Some stylists have maids who hand them the rollers, clips, and pins. More often the stylist keeps his equipment in a tray, which he gives to you, and you are to hand him the items—endpapers, rollers, clips, or picks as he needs them, one at a time. Pay attention while your hairdresser sets your hair. He will love you for it, and you will have a free lesson on how to take care of your hair between visits. Watch how he puts up the rollers and how he fashions the clip curls. Notice how he winds your hair. Ask him why he does some of the things he does. There is no hairdresser who does not want his customer to be able to help her hairdo herself.

Before going under the dryer pick up the magazine you will read—just one; you can pop out when you want another. Don't sweep the rack clean, leaving none for other customers. If you're a smoker, be sure there is an ash tray handy before you make yourself comfortable. The dial of the dryer is usually set at "hot." Try to stay under that temperature for as long as you can. Your hairdresser works against a deadline; those who lounge under a "cool" dryer delay his whole day's schedule. And don't keep asking if you're dry yet. Be patient; your hair must be bone-dry at brush-out time to insure a long-lasting set.

Now back to the styling table (replacing the magazines on the way and donning your dress again if it's an over-the-head one) for the final stage. Your hairdresser will now show you why it is that women still do go to beauty salons. He had a vision of the finished style when he first saw you and examined the contours peculiar to your face. Now, in arranging your hair, he is carrying out this vision. Don't bother him while he does this. Watch him, so you'll remember how and what he does. If you are dissatisfied with some part of the result, ask him politely, when he is finished, if he will alter that part. But remember that a set falls into place only after a few hours have elapsed, when the hair has cooled, relaxed and settled into its lines.

You now have a new hairdo. Thank your hairdresser. If he's the owner, as we have said, you need not tip him. If he is not, place the tip in his jacket pocket or hand it to him. The shampoo girl and maid, if either attended you, also deserve tips. When paying your bill, you should make your next appointment, to assure getting a convenient time. Above all, don't expect a Friday or Saturday appointment to be available to you if you telephone the night before those very busy days in any salon.

What if you live in a small town where there is either no hairdresser or the local salon's repertoire hasn't progressed beyond the poodle cut or a rigid finger wave? Obviously, you can't have a haircut by mail. Now your coiffure question becomes a do-it-yourself project—almost. The very first thing you should do is discover the best salon in the nearest city of some size. Study the ads in that city's Sunday papers and choose a salon in that city's best fashion store or, again, one that advertises quality, custom service—not an assembly-line, cut-rate coif. Your trips will be infrequent, so you can afford to spend a little more for the best. Make your appointment with a member of the salon's styling staff, and when you see him be frank in discussing your problem. Tell him how often you'll be able to visit the salon. A good stylist prefers an every-six-weeks-patron who firmly demands and gets his finest artistic efforts (and is a good "ad" for his work) to an every-week client who sets lower standards. Insist, first of all, upon a cut of moderate, manageable length. Between-trims growth should not raise new problems, so an ultrashort shaping whose neatness would demand two-weeks-hence re-shaping is out of the question. Your cut, of course, should be preceded by an analysis of your hair type and texture. Ask, too, that it be planned for setting and styling in several different ways and observe very carefully while the stylist is setting your hair. He'll be glad to show you ways in which the style may be varied between salon visits, and how to set it yourself. Some stylists will even equip you with a diagram of the setting you like so that you can put up your own do between visits to the salon.

When you judge a salon that's new to you—one whose reputation you know nothing about, you should know what to look for in judging it. There are state laws governing the operators, the conduct and the cleanliness of the salon. They are for your protection. Not every state has all these laws on its books, but here's a summary of most of the regulations in force:

Licenses are required of the manager, his staff and for the salon itself. There is usually a minimum education requirement—at least eight grades of school in some states, at least two years of high school plus training in a school of cosmetology—plus an examination. Licenses may usually be revoked on proof of noncompliance with state regulations. It is usually required that licenses be displayed in a prominent place.

Personnel operating a salon is regulated by law. Of course, it's hard for you to judge—but if the salon has been granted a license, you can be sure that its personnel are free of disease, have passed physical examinations, are of good moral character, don't use drugs, and have been trained in the art of cosmetology. They have to meet these requirements to obtain a license—and the state boards of cosmetology make periodic examinations and inspections (without warning) to check on them.

Treatment permitted in a salon is regulated by law in many states; and a distinction is drawn between purely cosmetic treatments like massage, applying lotions, and so forth—and medical treatment designed to cure ailments. A beautysalon operator is simply that; he is not, nor should he pretend to be or be asked to be a doctor, druggist, or curer of such things as warts.

The salon should be a separate unit with a separate entrance, even if it is conducted from the proprietor's home. Floors should be of nonabsorbent material. They should be kept reasonably free of hair, dirt, and debris. By reasonably, the law means that it recognizes that during a haircut, some hair always falls to the floor. But the floor should be swept regularly and kept well-scrubbed. Walls, too, should be washable or easily cleanable—including the woodwork. This is also true of the furniture, which explains why so many beauty-salon chairs are covered with plastic or simulated leather. Ventilation should be good, and you should have the feeling that the salon has fresh air entering from somewhere. Lighting should be adequate so the operator—and you—can see his work. This is especially necessary for coloring work. Running water both hot and cold should be in constant supply and should be applied by means of a spray.

Equipment includes sterilizers which should be a part of the salon's sanitary furnishings. There are quite a few methods of sterilization; the important point is—is the method in use? All tools should be sterilized, either by heat or chemical, before re-use. Towels should be kept in a closed linen cabinet and a fresh one used for each customer. When it has been used, the towel should be placed in a closed container. The "hair cloths" used to cover your clothes while you have your hair cut should be laundered frequently—and you should have a fresh piece of linen or paper around your neck, protecting it from contact with the hair cloth. Head rests should be protected with fresh, clean paper or linen. Shampoo boards and drains and the surrounding area, should be scrubbed after each patron has been shampooed. In some states these, too, must be sterilized. Head coverings, hair nets, drying hoods—any protective covering should be laundered or sterilized after each use and kept in covered containers between uses. Hairpins, rollers, clips, and other setting implements should be kept in covered containers and sterilized whenever possible. Permanent-wave supplies should be in closed containers and cleaned after every use.

Creams and other lotions should be taken from their jars with a spatula or a bit of cotton, never with the hand. This is a tip worth remembering for home use. It's so easy to use a cotton pad and you avoid the risk of reinfecting your skin or scalp. Creams should be kept covered when not in use. Powder puffs, dusters, and sponges should not be used—for the obvious reason that they transmit infection from person to person. Disposable paper or cotton pads are better. Open boxes of powder or other make-up set out for your use may seem like a friendly service, but they, too, are a possible source of infection and are prohibited in most states. Nail-white pencil, alum, or styptic pencils are all forbidden by many of the states. Powdered alum may be applied with sterilized gauze or cotton. The solid types of these products could transmit infection. Brushes and combs should be clean for each customer—and therefore, the operator needs a large supply. Some states specify twelve of each. You can tell if your operator has enough by seeing if he uses a clean instrument on *you*. Permanent endpapers used for cold waves should be discarded after each use. The cotton pads used to protect your ears and hairline while your hair is drying should be discarded after use; the emery boards your manicurist uses should be discarded; and her manicuring instruments sterilized. Eyebrow pencils should be sharpened after being used once; and tweezers sterilized after each use.

Uniforms should be clean, launderable, and worn by every salon employee. Hand washing should be routine. A beauty-salon employee should wash his hands before and after working on your hair. Paper drinking cups should be available, and soap dispensers should be in lavatories.

Impetigo or other fungus infections are all transferable; therefore an operator is not permitted to work on a customer suffering from these ailments. And they are all "catchable" if a salon doesn't live up to the law.

As we have said, not all states incorporate every one of these regulations. Some have long, rigid statutes that dictate almost every phase of beauty-salon operation; others have short laws that take only a sheet of paper to outline. But all of the laws are designed to protect you and your hairdo. We think it's important for you to know about these laws for several reasons: first, to help you judge a new salon which you've never before patronized; second, because if your state doesn't have a complete law, you may want to know what other laws exist for your own guidance; and third, because some of the sanitary laws are worth adopting in your own home. When you see a flagrant violation of the law in a salon you visit, it is your duty to report it to the state board of cosmetology or to your department of health if the proprietor refuses to rectify the trouble. It isn't fair to the many reputable beauty-salon operators to shrug your shoulders and let it go.

For instance, several states require a patch test before a permanent is given or a hair coloring applied. But not every state requires this. If yours doesn't, it's up to you to remind your operator that you want a patch test not just the first time she gives you a permanent or hair coloring, but every time. (Sensitivity may be developed by an individual at any time, despite her never having had an allergy before.)

There are ways in which some careless and lazy operators will cut corners and weasel around rules. Slipping the same comb back into a paper wrapper so that it looks as if you were getting a fresh one—or keeping the sterilizer filled with ordinary water—are but two examples.

In many states, it's illegal for a school of cosmetology to charge for the services of its students. That's why you can often get a free hairdo at the demonstration class of a beauty school. You take a chance, of course, that the student you happen to get isn't a budding genius!

In Massachusetts, an operator is prohibited from smoking while applying hair spray or lacquer to a customer's head. That's a safety tip worth noting for home use. And, as a matter of fact, every state should enforce this.

It has been the combined effort of good hairdressers throughout the country, with the assistance of public-spirited individuals—clients like you—who have helped bring these laws about. All but one state in the union (the exception is Virginia) have laws today governing the licensing and operating of beauty salons and barber shops. Some, of course, are more stringent than others. When you trust yourself to a hair stylist, you are running the risk of infection unless his standards are as high as those you maintain in your own home. Be grateful that your state has some standards; but it's up to you to look for an operator who believes in *maximum* standards.

CHAPTER V

At Home with Your Hairdo

Once you've found the hairdo for you, your problem will be one of maintenance. Even if you visit a hairdresser once a week, between trips to the salon or beauty shop you'll be on your own, practicing a little home hairdoing. Of course, if you're a do-it-yourselfer, you'll be more deeply involved in the art of hairdressing. In either case, you must have the proper equipment.

Time was when Great-grandmother had a bowl, a pitcher, a bar of castile soap, lemon juice, a comb, and her faithful brush. That, plus a hand mirror and a bit of pomade, constituted her hair-grooming equipment. And who's to say she was less or more lovely, that her hair was a brighter or duller crowning glory? We know that we're luckier than she because today beautiful hairdos are possible for every woman —not just a few who were born with lovely locks. We're luckier because of the myriad modern products for hair care at our command and the wonderful taken-for-granted goodies like hair dryers, water at any temperature, shower sprays, and daylight lighting indoors—all designed to make hairdoing and grooming an effortless everyday routine. And it can be almost effortless if you organize a hairdo corner in your home to take full advantage of these twentieth-century luxuries.

Organize you must, or the paraphernalia you acquire for

home hair care could (and often does) become a chaotic (and unsanitary) clutter in your medicine cabinet and/or your dressing table. If you're just beginning home hairdoing, you're lucky and can start fresh. If not, take stock, toss away worn-out, useless, and stale items, and make a clean beginning of organizing.

Where will you do your hair? In the bathroom, a dressing room, your bedroom? Once you've chosen the most convenient corner for work, then set up your storage area as close to it as possible. Check the work center on these important points: How is the illumination? Is there both overhead lighting and enough light around the mirror? Is the mirror large enough, and if it is not three-way, is your hand mirror for back viewing of adequate size? Is your work chair or stool the proper height? Now check your shampoo spot. If you shower-shampoo that's one good way. If you basin-or-tub shampoo, then an important piece of equipment is a shampoo spray. Some modern basins have a built-in attachment. But a less-than-a-dollar attachment for faucets that is simply a flexible hose with a spray head works admirably for the very necessary thorough rinsings after shampooing.

Now for the somewhat formidable list of items and supplies you'll need to do a professional job at home. There are basics and necessaries plus nice-to-haves, special aids, and little luxuries. Depending on how often you're playing hairdresser to your tresses, you will stock more or less and perhaps none of certain items. If you're an habitual home hairdoer, you'll buy large economy sizes of some products (or if more than one member of your household uses the same product). Use this chart as a check list for taking inventory of presently owned items and as a shopping guide for additions and replenishings:

BASIC SUPPLIES	NECESSARY TOOLS
Shampoo	Rollers in
After-shampoo rinse	various sizes
(if needed)	Clips
Color rinse	Bobby pins
(if used)	(if used)
Setting lotion	Hairpins
Conditioning cream	(for extra-
(if needed)	long hair)
Hair spray	Plastic picks
	(if needed)
	Large comb
	Rattail comb
	Hair brush
	(for daily
	brushing)
	Styling brush

SPECIAL AIDS	LUXURIES & NICE-TO-HAVES
Shampoo brush	Sleep cap
Hair dryer with	Plastic hair-
hood	dressing cape
Three-way mirror	Drawer organ-
Shower cap	izers
Setting net	Kit or plastic
Endpapers	bag for
	rollers, etc.

SPECIAL AIDS	LUXURIES & NICE-TO-HAVES
Plastic gloves (for coloring)	One or more hairpieces
Heat cap for conditioning treatments	Wig Automatic scalp massager
Cellophane tape	Barrettes,
Cotton squares	bows, or
Mesh foundation for French twist (if needed)	other ornaments

NOTE: Permanent wave kits and permanent hair coloring and lighteners are not included because these items should not be stored for long periods of time. For details about permanent waving, see Chapter IX; for hair coloring, see Chapter X.

Now that you've checked your needs, let's examine some of the items you'll be buying. Tools, for instance; and the most interesting of these, the roller, is one of today's greatest boons to hair setting. Rollers (with their working partner, clips) are the basis for all the beautiful hairstyles you see. And they come in almost as many varieties as hairdos. You'd do well to get acquainted with the different kinds, discover their individual purposes, and see how your hairdresser uses different ones in different ways in your setting. This list, of course, does not describe every single roller made (one look at the vast array at your variety store's hair-goods counter will show the impossibility of that), but it does indicate the varieties available, along with some of their advantages. For perfect hair setting, you need a good wardrobe of rollers, of types and sizes suited to your particular style and your special kind of hair. Costs vary, on the average, from five to thirty cents apiece.

INDEX OF ROLLERS

Wire-and-mesh or brush-rollers

A spiral of wire, covered by mesh of horsehair or nylon (or similar synthetic). These have the advantages of quick drying, of very wide range of sizes. Some come with brushes in center for neater rolling of hair ends; endpapers should be used on those without brushes. They can be fastened with picks, clips, or with the special long roller bobby pins.

Plastic rollers

Also in a variety of sizes, these are made of polyethylene or similar plastic. Easily washed, they are the most sanitary and safe to use for soft, body home permanents. Some have brushes; others come with flexible grip-teeth or a separate brush for rolling. Use picks, clips, or pins to fasten.

Foam rollers

Most comfortable for sleeping, these are tubes of plastic foam with flexible, coated wires for fastening or, in the large size, with plastic prongs for holding. Colors are pretty pastels.

Self-fastening plastic rollers

These come in a size range similar to that of plain plastic rollers but have their own fastening device attached, eliminating the need for other picks or clips. All-plastic ones are safe for permanents. Some have clamps to go over the finished roll; some have clamps to go over the ends before you roll; some use elastic fasteners. They may have brushes or tiny teeth to grip hair; if not, it's best to use endpapers.

Vinyl rollers

Soft, rubbery, comfortable, and firmer than the plastic foam. Most have their own fasteners. These, too, can be used for home-permanent curling.

Magnetic rollers

Made of firm synthetic, specially treated so that wet hair clings to the roller, for neater, smoother winding. In large sizes, but not very comfortable for sleeping. Fasten with clips or long bobby pins.

Metal rollers

Sometimes used for special styles, as the page boy. Usually come with self-fasteners. Cannot be used ever for permanent waving.

NOTE: Among old-fashioned types still in use (but not producing the satisfactory results of the modern ones listed) are leather curlers with wire fasteners, aluminum or other metal slim rollers with metal spring clamps. New developments to watch for: rollers which need no clips or picks to anchor, softer rollers, which hold their shape and the shape of the curl but are easier to sleep on.

Those are the basic roller types, but just as important as the kind you use is the size of roller you use. Your hair—its strength, how easily it curls, how long the curl lasts—is one factor determining the sizes you use; strong, easily curled hair takes larger, thicker rollers, while hair with less natural curl needs a thinner roll. Your style is the second factor. Notice how carefully your hairdresser selects the roller for each position of your setting; he knows the importance of size—and so should you. Here then is a guide—and the dotted lines are *actual* size:

GIANT, LONG
Use these for very bouffant,
bouncy styles, when hair is strong,
curls easily. Used at crown,
sometimes at sides when deep
full waves are wanted.

GIANT, SHORT
Use shorter length
for closer placement
of rollers,
especially to give
crown height.

JUMBO, LONG
Less easily curled hair
needs these smaller—but still very large—
rollers for bouffant dos.
Also make smooth dos, side
width, page-boy ends.

JUMBO, SHORT
Use when wrapping
narrow strands,
in setting short
temple curls or
crown fluff.

LARGE, LONG
*Frequently used for top back,
lower side settings, sometimes when
narrower waves are wanted.*

LARGE, SHORT
*Shorter width permits
close placement in
back settings.*

MEDIUM, LONG
*Use at ends, back, when loose
waves or curls are wanted.*

MEDIUM, SHORT
*Handy for over-ear,
upper-nape placement.*

SMALL, LONG
*Use for hairline curls, for
other hard-to-curl areas.*

SMALL, SHORT
*Also for hairlines,
for narrower strands.*

TINY, LONG
Only for difficult-to-curl spots.

TINY, SHORT
For tiniest nape curls.

Clips, picks, bobby pins, and hairpins are varied too. Here is a quick guide to help you select what you will need:

INDEX OF CLIPS, PINS, PICKS

Clips

In various sizes from tiny (1 inch) to long (4 inches), clips are used mainly for pin curls and for holding some kinds of rollers (although rollers are often packaged for sale with the clips to be used if necessary). Clips are constructed with single or double prongs, flat, curved, or rippled. Most are metal (aluminum, stainless steel), some are plastic and metal, and a few are all plastic. Longest clips are used mainly for holding sections of hair, securing rollers, or making and holding deep dips (like the wide finger wave). Those curved to hug the head are best for holding a deep wave. The most popular pin-curl clip is flat, double-pronged, and a standard 1⅞ inches long. These have replaced the bobby pin for setting pin curls because they slide easily and hold firmly. They can also be used for holding rollers. Tiny clips, single or double-pronged, are good for setting very fine, short nape hair. Prices vary for all of these, but the cost of the average short clip is about eight for thirty cents and for the very long double-prong ones, four for forty cents.

Pins

Bobby pins, for the most part, are interchangeable with clips, though today the majority of women prefer clips. Bobby pins are less conspicuous and may be used for fastening French twists, chignons, and hairpieces. They are also used in making stand-up, or sculptured, pin curls as opposed to the flat ones. Most bobby pins now have plastic or rubberized tips over the metal ends to protect hair. They come in various lengths, but the average ones favored by most are about 2 inches. In hair-matching colors—black, brown, silver, gold— a dime gets ten, twenty, thirty, and sometimes more, depending on the quality of the metal and the coating (often enamel) or finish used. Look for smooth-sided ones, crimped or straight, with coated tips to prevent hair damage.

Hairpins are still in fashion, and new uses and new hairdos come up for them all the time. A must for the girl who wears her locks uncut, for put-ups, for chignons, topknots. Wire ones in very small sizes to match hair color are indispensable for anchoring a switch invisibly (used two at a time, one up and one down for double security). Giant, super-strong ones are great for holding up very thick, long hair. Bone, plastic, tortoise pins, plain or decorative, are often in vogue as decorative embellishments for hairdos with hairpiece arrangements. The wire ones cost about a dime for thirty or more and up. Plastic ones in various colors average about ten cents for four or more. Bone and tortoise are more expensive.

Picks are the modern roller fastener and are made of nylon (the toughest variety) or plastic in pretty colors. Some are just straight pins with little round tops; others are T-shape with split centers—all look like hors d'oeuvre picks. Average cost: fifty to sixty for sixty cents.

Combs and brushes

Next, let's guide you to some suitable combs and brushes. Did you know there's a comb for hair with dandruff? A comb whose chief function is applying permanent-wave solution? A comb for fine hair, for coarse hair, for rolling, for untangling —a comb, in fact, for almost every purpose, every type of hair? True, it's not likely you'll ever see all these combs in use. Most are for professional stylists, and most stylists have a favorite few types which they use according to the style being set or the type of hair. Combs are made of metal, plastic, hard rubber, tortoise, and sometimes bone or bamboo (used in the Orient). Basically, you need but two—a dressing comb and a rattail comb. The former is your usual dressing-table comb, a long one with fairly long teeth and the teeth coarse at one end, fine at the other. Look for one that's easy for you to handle, is strong enough for the density and texture of your hair, and has teeth crafted with smooth edges and tips. The rattail comb has a long, slim handle that tapers to a point and comes with fine or coarse teeth, either deep or shallow. The tip of the comb is an aid in all hairdoings at home and in the salon. Its purpose: lifting individual sections of hair, particularly back-brushed or teased sections. Other combs of interest that may serve you in your home hair care: the multiple-row comb with flexible nylon teeth that combs, brushes, and massages. The comb comes with or without a rattail handle and may have two or three rows of teeth. The comb-brush combines comb and brush, is handy for your handbag or for traveling. On one side are bristles (nylon or natural), good for brush-ups, on the opposite side, teeth; the handle is a rattail. Your selection of a hairbrush—and two are better than one—is most important. For complete details about brushes, see Chapter VII.

Home hair dryers

For you who do most of your hair care yourself, a home hair dryer is more than just a nice-to-have; it's a must. The variety from which to choose grows greater every year and the kinds range from no-nonsense, do-the-job basics to fairly fanciful last-word luxuries.

The first and most important advantage of the home dryer is its obvious purpose of saving time—literally hours—in your hairdoing schedule. Even the primitive instruments available in the twenties and thirties answered that basic need; their steady blast of heat, pushing the air before them, did succeed in drying the hair more quickly than unaided room circulation, but the difference was slight. This function was performed in distinctly limited fashion: The hair dryer was hand-held (a heavyweight too), could dry only a tiny section of hair at one time, and had only one heat level (usually searing). Similar dryers—known as the "pistol" type, because of the manner in which they are held—are still available, may be useful to a certain extent as spot dryers of small areas, and cost only a few dollars. But nowadays, for very little more money, very much more sophisticated devices may be purchased. Now, depending on its length and texture, your hair may be dried in as little as half an hour, permitting before-work or before-date shampooing and setting. You can read—or write or sew or cook or even telephone—while your hair dries.

The great modern innovation in home hair dryers is the hood that slips over your set, enabling you to dry your whole head at once (as your hairdresser does), rather than section by section. It is connected to the motor-driven drying unit by an extension sleeve or—in the most up-to-date models—a lightweight, flexible hose resembling that on a vacuum cleaner. Many include a variety of extra conveniences. Whatever dryer you consider buying should have four basic characteristics. The drying unit itself should be sturdily constructed and designed so that it is not easily tipped over. There should be a control switch on the drying unit. And because it is an electrical device you will be using in close proximity to yourself, safety is important. Choose a dryer that carries the respected approval tag of Underwriters' Laboratories. Finally, the hood should be washable (most are).

Beyond the basics, dryers differ vastly in their type of construction and the conveniences they offer. Chief among these differences is hood and hose construction; each of these falls into two basic types. The hood may be a simple plastic bubble with one warm-air entrance and numerous perforations that permit the air to escape—or you can choose the diffusion-type hood that channels the air between two layers and into the hood from all directions, thus preventing an uncomfortable "hot spot." The hose, as previously noted, may be flexible, permitting movement of your head while your hair is drying; or it may be a simple plastic-sleeve extension of the hood itself, requiring sit-still hair drying so the sleeve does not collapse and cut off air flow. In addition, your special needs may suggest consideration of other factors. If you travel a lot, choose the kind of dryer that comes in its own travel case—and test it for portability. Some models offer extra-large hoods to accommodate extra-large-roller settings. Comfort-minded women should look for a wide range of heat settings; some dryers merely switch on—others offer several settings from "cool" up to "high" heat.

An increasing number of dryers now offer not only quick, competent drying equipment, but a host of other accessories and attributes too—some are nice-to-own conveniences, others pure luxuries. They include (each is featured by one or more models): a shoulder strap permitting walking about while hair dries; carrying-case accessories—mirror, nail dryer, nail buffer, nail file, compartments for clips and rollers; brush and comb that attach to the air hose for no-set drying; chic milliner-designed hoods; a top-of-the-hood reach-in window for touch-testing degree of dryness; a case that functions as a separate overnight bag; a voltage-adapter for foreign travel. By and large, the extras cost a little more—but it's not necessarily so in all cases. If you're considering the purchase of a home hair dryer, consider your needs first of all—and then shop around and compare.

Shampoos and hair sprays

Your hair-care supplies include shampoo (the kinds and character and uses of these are detailed in Chapter VIII), conditioning cream—if you need it for damaged hair (discussed in Chapter XII)—color rinses (see Chapter X), setting lotion (see the next chapter and also some tips from the professional stylists in Chapter XX), and hair sprays. These last —the hair sprays—are another of our present-day beauty-aid miracles.

Practically every hair spray you can purchase these days (except color sprays) can serve your hairdo needs in several ways. All behave, basically, as fast-drying firmers and may therefore be used to hold a finished hairdo in place. Some are used in setting to firm or hold the curls and waves. And the lacquerless ones—which contain an ingredient that relaxes at the touch of a damp comb—also function as aids to midday or midevening redoing. What's more—as if these three talents weren't amazing enough—many sprays now incorporate extra benefits: as you spray, you apply special conditioners (such as lanolin), moisturizers, proteins, sunscreens, anti-humidifiers, or unique elements designed for individual problems and conditions.

Sprays are designed in various formulas to control hard-to-handle tresses and to protect the hairdo. Your problem is to find the spray suited to your hair and your hairdo's needs. When you buy, read the labels—and the small print—first. Sprays without lacquer tend to give less stiffness, less rigid control. If, on the other hand, you have extra-incorrigible hair or you wear your hair in a high and delicately balanced do, then you'll want the stronger support of a firmer spray.

For this reason, you'll find several makers offer more than one spray type.

Any product performs to best advantage when used according to directions, and for the purposes specified; that's why detailed instructions are provided. Sprays are no exception. So read what's printed on the can before you buy. You'll find, first, that all the labels include certain precautions (keep away from eyes, don't incinerate can—a must on all aerosol-packaged sprays). Heed them. Usually you're also told to spray from a distance—varying from seven to twelve inches. This will determine how light or heavy a misting your hair receives. Suggested uses, with full directions, are usually given. These vary according to the spray's special formula, but here are the usual procedures: For setting, wait till hair is nearly dry, lightly spray and roll each section at a time, and let hair dry completely. For combing naturally wavy hair, spray first, then comb and arrange. For holding your finished coif, arrange in final fashion and then spray. For recombing (this with nonlacquer types), simply rearrange with dampened comb. For a special quick-set, set, then spray and let dry or spray lightly (no water), set, let dry.

If your hair presents a special problem, read further. Some sprays are made specifically for fragile hair, especially if it's tinted or lightened. These are planned to prevent any adverse reactions that may affect the color, texture, or porosity. Many include protein, lanolin, or other conditioners; these will help if your hair tends to dryness. Some come in several formulas for various hair types—dry, oily, etc. Some are geared to climate or other externals, with sun-shields or dust-repellers. And now, you can also buy hypo-allergenic hair sprays.

You'll see sprays in a truly amazing variety of sizes—from a ¾-ounce purse cylinder to containers whose contents range from four to twenty-four ounces. If you're simply sampling, select small sizes. But when spray's part of your grooming routine (it should be) and you've settled on the one for you, you'll find the per-ounce cost less in larger sizes.

Special aids

Special aids for long-hair wearers (and see Chapter XVIII for how to handle long hair) are such items as French roll foundations made of horsehair or nylon mesh (costing as little as about thirty cents), doughnut-shaped chignon rolls of the same material (costing as little as forty cents, approximately), hair buckles for upswept dos in all degrees of decorativeness and ranging in price from as little as twenty-five cents, ornamented and plain holding combs from twenty-five cents up, practical flexible combs in strips with holding teeth, elastic-coated rubber bands for ponytails with or without bows or jewels and flowers, ring-combs for slipping over ponytails, mesh rolls for setting page-boy hairdos—all of these to be found in dime stores and wherever hair notions are sold. Study the counters for these assists and find the ones that fit your needs.

CHAPTER VI

The Well-set Do and How It's Done

Maybe you're a teen trying to set your hair for the first time. Or, maybe you are a lot older and all your life have worn your hair in a bun you'd like to have cut off, but you're afraid you can't maintain a short style. For you, the first curl is the hardest. And it takes plenty of practice after that first all-thumbs attempt. But cheer up, even the least-nimble-fingered can cut pin-up time to as little as ten minutes (some whizzes have been known to do it in less).

The tips in this chapter not only will help the beginner but will also guide those who are more proficient in home hair setting, with special pointers on improving technique. The diagrams here show you all the basics you need to know, and the step-by-step photographs in the picture section of this book will show you details of the professional stylist's procedure. In that section, too, you will find photographs of classic, never-out-of-fashion hairstyles together with diagrams of roller-and-clip positioning for setting these styles. If you choose one of these styles to try, be sure that your hair is cut properly for the style. Consult your hairdresser (and read Chapter XVII on the subject of haircutting).

One of the best ways to begin learning how to set your hair is this: Don't attempt a whole hairdo, but right after you come home from the salon, pick up a single curl near your face where you can easily see it in your mirror. Use your thumb and index finger—of your left hand if you're a right-handed girl and with the right if you're a left-hander. Pull it (never fear: if it's a good set, this won't hurt it) and let it drop back into place. Which way does it curl? Toward your face? Pick it up the same way again, and pull it taut. Then, with the thumb and index finger of the opposite hand, smooth it into an arc and, beginning with the top, roll it smoothly and snugly close to the scalp in a circle. Wind it in the direction in which you saw the curl spring back into place. Tuck the tip inside the circle, hold it in place with one finger, and gently slide an opened clip or bobby pin (the former is easier on the hair and easier to manage) across one side of the curl and through the center. Practice it. When you've mastered that one, do the other pin curls in your new hairdo, rolling them forward or backward as they were set. If your coif involved roller setting as well as clip curls, you'll find that a clip placed here and there to hold the roller brush-out your hairdresser did for you will be enough to maintain your style overnight. Then spray—ever so lightly—with mild setting lotion, or just dampen the replaced clip curls with water, net the whole do, and you're set for the night.

Once you've mastered repinning the hairdo your hair-dresser has created for you, you're ready to try the whole thing on your own—i.e., after your home shampoo. Allow plenty of time (and patience) if this is your first attempt. Make sure you have the correct tools and enough of all of them (see the preceding chapter). Then proceed in an orderly fashion, this way:

1. Start with clean, freshly shampooed hair. Towel-pat excess water, but don't dry. Sit down before a three-way mirror (or with a good hand mirror available to check sides-and-back work).

2. Carefully comb hair through, being extra-careful with tangles and knots. Comb hair in the direction of the finished

style: parting where final part will be, combing without a part if there is to be none, combing out bangs (if any) in the direction of their ultimate brush-out.

3. If setting lotion is to be used, apply it on the first area to be set—preferably spraying it on. This is especially important if you tend to work slowly and your hair dries quickly.

4. Section hair into curl areas. You will work on only one section at a time and it's best to pin other areas out of the way (with oversize clips) to avoid confusion as you set one part. For most hair setting, it's best to start at the brow line first, work next on crown, then sides, back, in that order. Set ends, nape curls, cheek curls, bangs last, dampening them again if necessary.

5. Determine the direction of each roller or clip curl— either from a diagram provided by your hairdresser or from a hair-setting pattern (see photograph section) which clearly marks directions.

6. Use pin curls for close-to-the-head control. Use rollers for fullness, for curve without too much curl—the larger the roller, the wider the curve. Choose roller sizes according to hair texture too. The stronger your hair, the larger the roller, since the hair will hold the set longer; for the same size curl in finer hair, use a smaller roller.

Study the sketches below for how to wind and fasten rollers (and also see photographs in center picture section of this book). Take only as much hair to wind as your roller can comfortably hold—that is, a section on your scalp about one inch deep and slightly shorter in width than your roller. Part this off, comb it smoothly, and hold the strand straight up, slanted away from direction to be rolled. Place roller near scalp in front or in back of strand (depending on direction of desired wave) and slide it along strand to end. Wind, tucking ends in smoothly (or folding an endpaper over ends first) and catching any side wisps as you wind. Wind evenly, smoothly, never stretching or pulling, and, holding roller securely against scalp, slide a clip near base to hold in place or insert a pick through center from top to hold. Use the tip of a rattail comb to tuck in any wayward ends or wisps. If short clips are used for fastening, slide one in at each end of roller. If the next roller rests side-by-side with the first one, use one clip to hold two rollers together. Each roller should rest directly in the center of its section to avoid splits and separations in the finished hairdo.

Section hair first

Hold strand straight up

Hold two rollers with one clip

Clip curls are done as described in the first part of this chapter. Remember to keep curl flat, with the tip or end curled into the center of the curl. Crisscrossing two clips to hold curls is the old-fashioned way and often leaves marks on finished curls. Slide clip across top of curl, leaving center open. End curls and nape curls, when hair is short, are set in curves—or incomplete circles—so that curls will lie close and hug the head in the final brush-out. Curve curl into shape with fingers, tip of rattail comb, or simply by combing in a curved direction. Keep curl flat and clip in place flat against the head. For extra fluffiness in a style you may wish to make stand-up pin curls. You simply form the curl around your index finger at tip of strand, then roll curl down to scalp, so that curl stands up from head like a loop. Slide clip through center of base of curl, close to scalp. The resulting curl looks like a very small roller curl minus its roller. Cheek curls, when hair is coarse and curls easily, may be made easily by taping a piece of cellophane tape across the formed curl on the cheek. This technique may also be used to set flat bangs. Curve or comb bangs in direction desired, then secure with tape strip until set dries.

Clip curls, in general, should be set in rows, long or short depending on results desired. Two rows at the bottom of a hair setting will make a thicker curl or fluff than one. Two

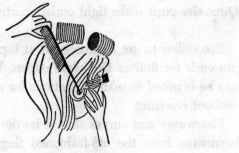

Curve curl into shape

Stand-up curl is clipped at base

Slide clip across top of curl

Tape cheek curls

rows set in opposite directions from each other will make a
wave. A large curl will make a looser, smoother effect than
a small one. The smaller the amount used in making a pin
curl, the longer-lasting the curl and the tighter the curl.

Dime-size curls make tight curls; quarter-size, looser; and so on.

Use rollers to get a smooth lift at top, back, or sides. Use pin curls for fluff or flat, close effects. Hair set with rollers can be brushed in many directions for many different styles without resetting.

Flat waves and curves should be done with a comb, or— borrowing from the old-fashioned finger-wave technique— using two fingers as pincers, to shape the direction after combing. Metal clamps designed for this purpose may be used for very deep, crested waves, but the effects produced are not compatible with today's hair fashions.

Classic page-boy settings can be given an assist with the use of a page-boy roll (a simple mesh tube). Simply comb damp hair over the roll and secure with pins or clips. More elaborate rolls have bands that fasten over the head and a net to cover hair, eliminating the need for pins and the danger of pin marks. If your own hair has little curl, the roll should be used for nightly putting up. Otherwise, this type of setting provides the smoothness and bounce that will last for several days.

There are several points to watch in your setting technique to avoid bent wisps and "fishhooks." If you can't keep the very ends of your hair from doubling under the roller as you wind a strand, then do use endpapers to counteract this. Some stylists prefer a bit of cotton wool over the fragile ends. If you use clamp-type rollers, insert another endpaper between roller and clamp before fastening. In the case of nape curls, guiches (cheek curls), and short bangs, remember that too many clips can spoil the curl. Use only one clip per curl whenever possible. If your hair is lightened often, it will tend to be more porous, hence more prone to bend, and clips can leave undesirable marks on overporous hair.

Once your hair is set, place a hair-setting net over all to hold the setting as it dries. Tuck little squares of cotton or facial tissue over your ears, under the net, and dry your hair at the lowest possible heat. This will take longer but will be easier on your hair and scalp. Use "high" heat indicator on your home hair dryer only when you're in a hurry. If your hair tends to frizz, set your hair when it is only slightly damp and remove clips and rollers before hair is completely dry— i.e., dry on the outside, but still damp on the inside. Then recover loosely with net and allow to dry thoroughly in the normal atmosphere.

If your hair has been dried electrically, allow it to rest and cool before brushing out. But be sure, before putting brush to your new set, that hair is bone-dry. For brush-out details, see the next chapter.

Practice makes perfect in home hair setting as with every-thing else. The angles of rollers and curls are important. Pay attention to them when you study hair-setting patterns. Curls set T-square straight across the back, row after row, will make a series of waves—big ones if big rollers were used, small ones if rollers were small. Rolling them at a slant— anywhere between horizontal and vertical—but parallel and using the same amount of hair for each one will make a wave pattern, a directional wave that might be more becoming to you. If you're after a this-way-that-way kind of wave, one that moves in a curved direction, you do this by angling too. But have your pattern firmly in mind before you set, and follow it, angle by angle. The slant of your rollers at the sides can change the final hairdo too. Slanted down, back from the face, they'll brush out into soft waves that give the appear-ance of length to the hair, perhaps covering the ears, and, if you wish, curling around forward. The opposite slant, one with rollers on an up-angle, will brush out with a lift to the side hair, giving it a shorter look that wings away from the face and changes your profile. At the top, an angle gives direction to top waves, fluffs, or bangs. If yours is a symmetrical do, well and good—your top setting of rollers will be symmetrical too. But if you want a directional wave, follow the angled pattern.

Too tired to set your hair at night? Your husband hates to see you wearing rollers to bed? Your parents can't stand the sight of you running around in rollers and clips all afternoon? Then try setting in the morning. If you can allow forty-five minutes, your hairdo will be beautiful on arrival—at school, at P.T.A. meeting, at the office. Here's how: The moment you're out of bed—even before you brush your teeth—put your hair up, with rollers, clips, pins. Use whatever you normally choose to wind up curls and set waves. Then spray your entire set with your favorite wave lotion, a special curl spray, or a fine mist of plain water. Dampen difficult areas more than others, but do not soak the hair. Keep the spray container a foot from your head, and avoid those parts of your hairdo that do not really need setting. Most women who have had a good salon styling will find that only the nape ends and any cheek curls or wings need dampening. This takes—depending on your skill—from five to ten minutes. You're ready for tubbing, scrubbing, face fixing —another fifteen minutes. On with your underclothes, stockings and shoes, and to breakfast in your housecoat. Thirty-five minutes gone. Put on your dress or suit, gather accessories for departure. Then, and only then, you're ready for the brush-out. Use and keep handy for your "A.M. set" a little make-up cape or lint-free fabric to protect shoulders of your going-out clothes. Remove rollers, clips, et al., and brush out your set. You'll find it smoother, with fewer flyaway ends, because you haven't tossed and turned on it all night in bed. And for most hairdos, this amount of time is enough to maintain a well-coifed head. Keep hair-setting tools and accessories in a handy tray and always replace them as you finish each setting or put-up. A final once-over of hair spray, to keep hair in place through the day and to add extra gloss and sheen, is a good idea before you leave the house.

The use of a curling iron to revive a flagging hairdo should be approached with caution. The possibility of hair damage is great, but the iron properly used, can revive a sagging curl or setting in an emergency. Hair that is tinted, lightened, or color-rinsed should not be waved with an iron. Professional-type irons (available only to the professional at present) with special conditioning solutions that release from the rod as hair is being set are much more acceptable as "instant" wave makers.

If you do plan to use some new-to-you technique or tool for setting your hair, your best bet is to check your hairdresser on its use and the possibilities of its use on your hair. This is true for hair products as well.

CHAPTER VII

How to Brush Out Your Setting

The prettiest hairdo you've ever seen has undoubtedly enjoyed superior "brushmanship." That lovely, controlled, supersmooth coif depends for its appeal on luster, sheen, and texture—the result of absolute cleanliness and diligent brushing. And it's not only Grandmother's hundred-strokes-a-night that's important, but the setting brush-outs and through-the-day touch-up brushings as well.

Some hair stylists never use a comb at all but rely on a wardrobe of hairbrushes in every shape, size, and weight with every kind of bristle you can think of. How many can there be? For the hairdresser, there's the professional brush for short- and medium-length hairdos. He may also use a pair of military-type brushes to "envelope" the scalp when brushing it before a shampoo—stirs up circulation, sloughs off dry scalp flakes and dust and grime, and sends natural oils flowing healthily along the hair shafts. A miniature brush to coax curls into place after the big brush-out is often used by high-fashion stylists instead of a comb, with the result a softer, smoother individual curl where it's needed. All these brushes-of-the-trade are invariably made with natural bristles. Most hairdressers feel that the natural-bristle brush is kinder to the hair and insures against damage to the hair shaft. With one exception: The synthetic-bristle brush will "excite" hair into the poufs and fluffs necessary for the fully rounded coif. Once, however, the necessary bulk of hair is

created, the hairdresser will then switch to a natural-bristle
brush to satin-smooth the cocoon or outer layer of hair.

But what kind of brush should you own and use? Or
should you have more than one? You've dozens from which
to choose—at all prices, in all colors and shapes, and with
many kinds of bristles. One English firm exports over thirty
different varieties to us—with prices that range from $2.50
for a little postiche brush for curls and small hairpieces to
$1000 for a rare wild Siberian boar-bristle brush. There are
plastic-handled and satin-wood- or ebony- or cherry-, or teak-
handled brushes. There are brushes with refills of new bristles, brushes with black bristles, brushes with white-as-snow
bristles. When you choose yours, consider these factors: Is
your hair wiry, wild, coarse? You need a tough-bristled brush
that grips the hair and gives your scalp a thorough workout.
Baby-fine, wispy hair? A gentler-bristled brush for you—but
with long and short natural bristles to stroke as well as stimulate. Hair that lies flat and limp most of the time? Liven it
up with a synthetic-bristle brush (a good-quality one with
smoothly cut ends)—*after* you've given it its hundred daily
licks with a boar-bristle brush to improve its health and condition. Consider, too, the heft of a brush in your hand
when you're selecting one. Is it comfortable for you to grasp
and hold, and will it be strong enough yet lightweight enough
for you to endure the necessary amount of nightly brushing?

Ideally, your minimum wardrobe of brushes should be
three—one for preshampoo brushing (the grime-getter), one
for nightly conditioning, and a little one for styling and
touching up (this one's also nice to carry in your handbag).

Once equipped, you should know how to use your brush
or brushes. Very few people really know how to brush hair
properly. Here's what the experts—both brush makers and
hairdressers—say: Begin by brushing hair firmly back from

face. Brush next up and away from the neck, never down. Throw head forward as you bend from the waist. Brush briskly from the nape of the neck to the very ends of the hair. Keep stroke steady—don't tear at the hair. Give a slight twist to the wrist as you brush. This makes a brush stroke with a rolling motion that grips the hair, gently tugs the scalp to stimulate circulation. The upward, outward movement raises the hair, enabling bristles to massage and cleanse the scalp. Be sure to complete every stroke to the very ends of the hair. How many times? Two hundred? That's "brushmanship" if you're doing it right with the right brush for your hair. One hundred? That's Grandmother's rule. The more, the better—but we'd say you'd have a pretty healthy scalp with a mere fifty good, professional strokes.

Your common sense should tell you the benefits of daily brushing. It's the best treatment for dull, streaky hair, for excessively oily as well as excessively dry hair. Thin hair will soon look fluffier, thicker, more luxurious. Coarse and wiry hair can become tamer, more manageable. If it's flyaway, fine, and wispy hair, brushing will improve body, bring out highlights you'd never suspect were there. Think of your brush as a polisher, a buffer, and a stimulator. Then, think of it as a hair-styling tool.

Your hairdresser can tell you it's true: The success of your hairdo depends on three things: the haircut, the set, and the brush-out. Setting is discussed in Chapter VI, and the all-important cut later, in Chapter XVII. Here, we'll discuss the brush-out.

GUIDE TO BRUSH-OUT

You'll begin, of course, with hair that's bone-dry. Your equipment, spanking clean and thoroughly dry too: a firm-bristled hairbrush; a comb or slim teasing brush; a rattail comb. And you've a can of hair spray handy, too, properly selected for your kind of hair.

Remove clips and rollers, picks and papers—gently, please, without tugging or tearing. If hair's been dryer-dried, replace each curl in roller form, let it cool that way. Start right at the hairline and brush straight back—in long, vigorous strokes, blending all the curl lines together. It's this step, too, that removes any of the fine, nearly invisible residue left by many of the most effective setting solutions.

If your hair tends to dryness, dab a bit of cream hairdressing on the palm of one hand, rub hands together, then run them through your hair this way: slide fingers back from the hairline, up from the nape, close to the scalp. Brush again, now blending the curl lines still more, and being sure to carry your brush strokes the full length of each strand to distribute the hairdressing.

Up to now, you'll notice, we haven't taken your hairdo it-self, the special lines of your setting, into account at all. That's the way your hairdresser works, too; it's just at this point, when all your hair has been thoroughly brushed out and

Now, with your brush, begin to guide your hair into the lines defined by your setting. Details are not important now; work for over-all di-rection, moving the hair in large sections, concentrating on top and sides. Stop and check your progress now; use a hand mirror, and exam-ine your coif from all sides. What to look for: those areas that seem to be resisting your coaxing into line, those that will need some special attention or extra control.

brushed briskly through, that the really definitive styling of
the final look begins, and your do begins to assume its finished
lines. All the hair has been massed, with the last step, at the
back.

Now, use your comb or your teasing brush to mesh the strands that
might separate, to tame a stubborn cowlick, to add height and fullness
where needed.

Back to your regular hairbrush now for the final molding and smoothing. Let fingers help, too, now in drawing out a slim cheek curl, draping a wave, curving a flip. All done, just as you like it? Spray now —an even misting all around, holding the can upright and as far away as label directs.

Before the spray's quite dry, use the flexibility it gives you to adjust those last little touches: lift very, very lightly with rattail comb to pouf where fullness is needed—at the turn of the bangs or the rise of the crown; use fingers to fan out a flip or guiche, if needed.

A much misused form of hairbrushing is what is known popularly as "teasing" (also called back-brushing, back-combing, French lacing, and, in its worst form, "ratting"). Its practice in creating weird hair silhouettes and its incorrect execution, often leading to serious damage of the hair, are to be deplored. Properly done, teasing can play an important part in finishing a hairstyle, correcting a line or reviving a coif. Use a small brush or teasing brush (bristles are uneven) in most areas, a comb or teasing comb where hair is quite short. Here, then, is the proper way:

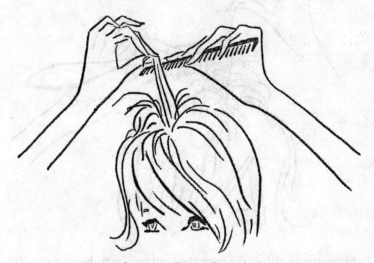

Start with one small strand, comb through.

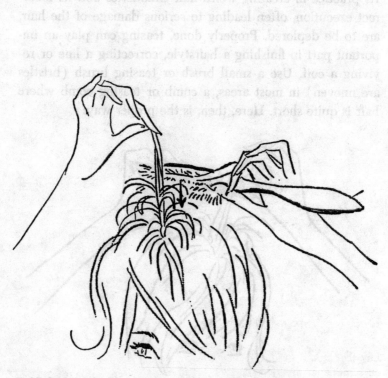

Hold the strand of hair out from the head and, with brush on under-side, start first stroke one inch from scalp; brush down. Start next stroke about an inch higher; brush down. Repeat to end of strand.

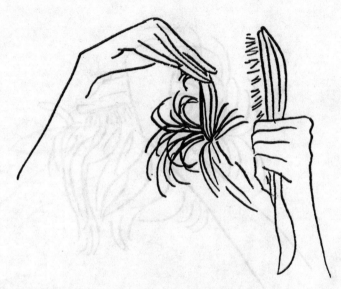

Lay that strand forward, work next on strand beneath or behind (or on same layer first, if teasing a wide area); tease in the same way, stroke by stroke.

After all strands in area are teased, brush smooth in layers with light strokes, starting with lowest—or last-teased—section. This is very important—prevents the "ratting" that causes damage.

Work in successive layers, smoothing lightly.

Now at top, or beginning of area where you started teasing, smooth whole area, always very lightly, only on the surface. You're finished—hair is pouffier, and because it's been done right the teasing is not matted, has not damaged the hair.

What to use? A small brush or teasing brush (bristles are uneven) in most areas, a comb or teasing comb where hair is quite short.

Now that you've developed this useful tool of teasing (with practice you'll be doing it better and better), you should know how best to put it to use to make it work best for you. Basically, what teasing does is straighten the hair—in a way it paralyzes the hair so that it acts as support, forming body from underneath. And so its main purpose is to give width or height in certain areas—not all over, but only where needed:

One place where teasing is needed is in a symmetrical hairdo that droops on one side. Teasing will pick it up. Spray lightly, then lift with a rattail comb to even it the way you want it.

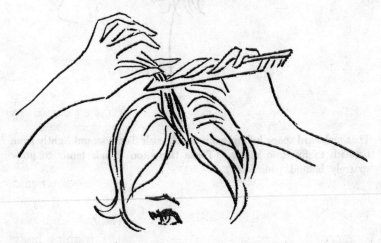

Good place for teasing—at a stubborn part that just won't disappear. With comb or brush (depends on how long the hair is there) tease strands at the part, then smooth over with light brush strokes.

That awkward space behind your cheek curl? Tease strand lightly from beneath to fill it in nicely. (Tease there too if hair tends to grow sparsely behind your ears.)

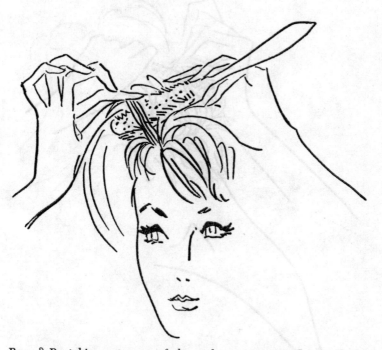

Bangs? By taking out some of the curl, teasing turns flyaway bangs into well-behaved ones. For fluffy bangs you'll find teasing both sides of the strand—the under side and top side too—will achieve the desired bounce.

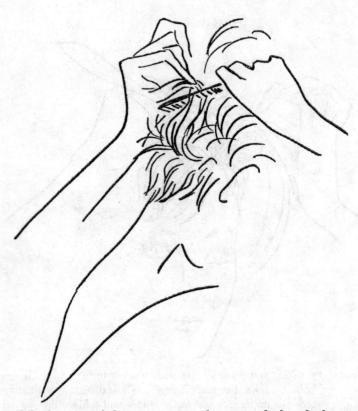

At difficult napes, it's best not to tease the very ends, but the layer of hair right above the nape.

If a drooping flip or roll is your problem, here's how teasing will help: First, tease the strands that make the flip, on both upper and under sides to give more body; then smooth the teased hair over your finger, using your rattail comb; a light brushing to smooth, and there you are!

Don't overdo teasing. And always do it gently. It may also be used for special-occasion coifs—but, unless you become very proficient, leave that to your professional hair stylist. To avoid tangles in combing through teased hair, begin with the undermost layer of hair and continue just as you would when combing after a shampoo. Never yank, pull, tug, or tear. And remember, teasing is only an aid to a style—not an excuse for one.

How to Have Height without Teasing Your Hair

One way to give extra height to your hairdo is to put a knot or twist up there. Hair fairly long and all one length works best for this.

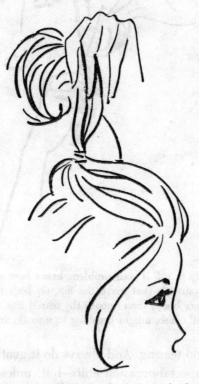

Section off top hair and pull all of it back from the brow; fasten close to head with coated-rubber band.

Divide the fastened strand in two; twist one half to form a rope-like strand and wrap around band or into a knot. Fasten with hairpins.

Twist second half and complete knot or coil, fastening with pins and hairpins.

Another way is to lift hair by crisscrossing strands at the top.

Start by brushing all hair back. Then section off a strand at the front and bring to one side smoothly.

Now section off a strand behind the front one and bring to the opposite side, lifting carefully and brushing top lightly only to smooth.

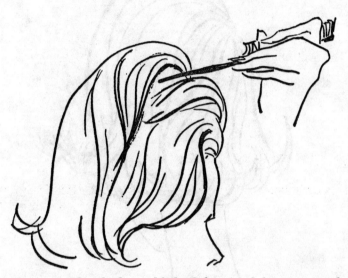

Do the same with a third strand behind the second, bringing strand to same side as the first. Again smooth strand gently. Then use rattail comb to lift up strands, separating them slightly.

Back will have a swing to one direction.

One of the prettiest methods makes height by curling or petaling top hair. Do it this way:

Section off top hair and brush back into full strand.

Fasten hair back with a wide comb; do it by placing comb at an angle, pushing hair forward so that it poufs on top.

Now curl ends forward or to the side in little petals. A mist of spray
will help hold them in position.

Using an opposite-direction setting is another height-adding method. This works best on fairly long hair, to give the height needed:

Start by sectioning off top hair. Roll first roller from side.

Continue with rollers, turning all in same direction.

When setting is dry, remove rollers and brush in opposite direction. Use rattail comb to lift lightly.

A good way to emphasize height is with a ribbon or other device, such as a comb or barrette:

Section off top hair, brush back, and fasten with a comb; blouse the hair forward as you tuck in the comb.

Now tie band or ribbon around the raised hair, fastening well in back to hold. Ends may drape over the ribbon or not, depending on hair length.

A handy trick, this way of creating height. You do it by
using a curl or roll under the hair to add extra bulk:

Section off a large strand of hair on the crown area, leaving plenty of
hair in front to make the finished line.

Coil the strand into a curl or roll; fasten well with bobby pins.

Now brush front hair over curl, layer by layer, to keep the top airy.
Fasten in back with comb, or lightly on sides with hairpins.

And of course there's the hairpiece, greatest height-adder yet. You can use hairpieces any number of ways, depending on the piece itself. Here's one way:

Shape the hairpiece into a bun or twist or what you will. Fasten it firmly to the crown, using both hairpins and bobby pins.

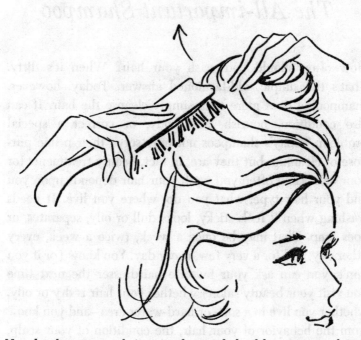

Now brush your own hair up and around the false piece, so that it blends in. A single hairpin, used as a comb, helps control and guide single strands.

Drawings in this chapter by Ray Porter.
© Dell Publishing Co., Inc., 1962, 1963.

CHAPTER VIII

The All-important Shampoo

How often should you wash your hair? When it's dirty. That's the simple, old-fashioned answer. Today, however, shampooing does more than simply cleanse the hair. It can also condition, nourish, add body, or correct a special problem. Today's shampoos not only serve their prime purpose of cleaning, but they are, in fact, beauty treatments for your hair. How often you wash your hair depends upon you and your hair type, what you do, where you live. It needs washing when it feels sticky, looks dull or oily, separates, or goes limp. That may be once a week, twice a week, every other day, and for a very few, every day. You know (or if you don't, you can ask your favorite hairdresser the next time you visit your beauty salon) whether your hair is dry or oily, whether you live in a soft- or hard-water area—and you know from the behavior of your hair, the condition of your scalp, how often you should shampoo.

So, name your hair type or your problem—dry, normal, oily, porous, fine, coarse, tinted, dandruff—there's a shampoo especially for you, right for your hair. Never use cake soap on your hair; use only a liquid or cream shampoo. If you live in a hard-water area, detergent shampoos will rinse out more readily than the soap shampoos. The oilier your hair, the harder-working shampoo it needs—one with deep-cleansing properties, one that is a soapless, nonoil-base type, adding no extra oils. Soap-based shampoos (derived from animal or vegetable fats) are designed for "average" or "normal" hair. For dry hair, those containing special emollients are formulated to protect as they cleanse, prevent defatting of the hair. Do dandruff's little white flakes mar the look of your coiffure? At last count, no fewer than seventeen different shampoos were available nationally, offering dandruff-controlling properties (see *Dandruff*, Chapter XII). Is your hair the limp, lifeless, won't-sit-up-and-curl kind? Now several shampoo-makers incorporate protein compounds into shampoos, compounds with a special affinity for hair. What they do: strengthen the hair, add body and bounce, hence help your hair take and hold its set better. Their effects tend to be cumulative rather than immediate—so give the one you choose a fair trial period, at least four to six weeks.

Lusterless hair is such a widespread problem that more shampoo makers have concentrated on this than any other. Scores of shampoos are available for this kind of hair—shampoos expressly designed to add luster and sheen, leave hair shining. In this category, too, are the "color" shampoos—designed not to change hair color, actually, but to brighten and highlight it. Some lighten to a barely perceptible degree with the effect, a subtle glowing and brightening of your natural shade.

As hair coloring plays an increasingly important role in hair fashion, both shampoo and color makers have become aware of a new problem: Hair that has been lightened, toned, or tinted needs special protection. The new color is sometimes less stable than natural color, can be adversely affected by certain chemical elements in some preparations—and hair that has been bleached tends, often, to be especially dry, sometimes fragile. If your hair is lightened or tinted, do by all means choose one of the special shampoos designed to protect it—specially mild shampoos that condition as they cleanse. These shampoos are formulated for color-compatibility as well, to keep the hue true and prevent its sliding off shade.

Shampoo form is purely a matter of personal preference. You can select from creams, lotions, and liquids to suit your taste. Soon to come: aerosol shampoos, their premeasured lather dispensed instantly at the push of a button. Whatever shampoo you choose, be sure to read all the instructions and information on the label. Do not experiment willy-nilly. There are some shampoos that are just fine for the girl next door but may do serious damage to your type of hair.

Where you do your shampooing is again up to you. Whether it's in a washbasin, tub, or under a shower, make sure you have adequate water pressure so that you'll have a strong stream of water for thorough rinsing. There are handy spray attachments for tub or basin faucets, inexpensive, easily attached, and wonderful for producing a beauty-salon-type rinse.

Before every shampoo, clean all your combs and brushes. Remove hair from brushes with a comb. Then dunk in suds (liquid soap with a tablespoon of ammonia) and warm water. Don't soak them, just immerse for a few minutes so that bristles won't be weakened. For stubborn dirt on combs, use a comb cleaner or an old clean toothbrush. Rub brushes together, gently, to speed up cleaning. Rinse thoroughly, tamp on a clean terry towel, and place brushes on the towel, bristles down, to drain and dry. Let them dry naturally, not near a radiator or range.

Now for the actual shampoo routine: First, of course, is the preshampoo brushing to remove loose dust, tone up circulation. Brush thoroughly back from hairline, up from the nape, forward at top (see Chapter VII). You'll need to wash this brush along with the rest so you'll have a clean one for the brush-out of your setting.

To avoid waste, measure out enough shampoo for two sudsings (about ¾ ounce). An applicator bottle makes a handy container, controls the shampoo flow. For oily hair, this is especially good, so that you can section your hair and apply the shampoo evenly to disperse the oil on your scalp. If hair is exceedingly dry, less shampoo—about half an ounce— will be necessary.

Wet hair—lukewarm water is best for all shampooing. Apply half of measured shampoo. Work it into a rich lather, using finger tips—never nails. Gently massage the scalp, start- ing at hairline and working lather through to back. Then massage from the nape line to front. Pay special attention to area around ears, front and back and at temples. Rinse thoroughly with steady stream of water (hair will "squeak" when all shampoo is out). Apply remainder of shampoo and repeat the same lathering and massage. With the final rinse, apply water, rinsing for a full three minutes to be sure that every last vestige of the cleansing agent has been removed. The next steps depend on your kind of hair: If hair is brittle, dry, coarse, porous, curly, tends to mat and tangle, use a cream rinse. Work the rinse through the hair to the ends. Some cream rinses require dilution, so if you use one, be sure to follow label directions exactly. And, once more, rinse hair thoroughly with water (unless the cream rinse used directs that it be left in).

Now you're ready for the finale: Bring hair back from face, wrap it, turban-style, in a clean towel. Blot it to remove excess moisture. Don't rub it—hair is at its weakest when wet and if yours tends to break, this is its most vulnerable moment. When hair is no longer dripping wet, gently comb—and you're ready for setting. The electric hair dryers today are excellent for speeding up drying, but a note of caution: please, not too high a heat for too long a time lest you end up with dryer-than-dry or dried-out hair. Unless you're in a hurry, however, towel-blotting is best before your setting. Some perfectionists use nothing but linen towels to prevent lint deposits on hair. No matter the towel, the process is the same. Pat it dry, never rub it briskly while wet.

CHAPTER IX

Home and Salon Permanent Waves

Pity the poor permanent. For it's probably the most maligned, most misunderstood, most abused part of the whole beauty business. In the minds of many the mere word conjures up pictures of frizzy ends, fuzzy curls, and tight little corkscrew waves. For those about to embark on their first permanent wave, the moment is one of apprehension. Well, if you're one of those frightened ladies, fear not. Despite the widespread picture we've just painted, it's a fact that a permanent can be smooth, can be loose, can be a permanent that doesn't show at all.

Probably much of the distrust of permanents stems from way back, when the cold wave was first introduced. Many beauty operators, used to the heat-wave method of permanenting that required tension to make the wave, gave their cold waves the same way. They used tension in rolling the waves, and tension while rolling is a big "must-not" in giving today's permanents. The results were sometimes disastrous. And the memory of them has lingered.

That was clearly a case of misuse of the cold wave. Today, operators are used to the technique and more adept at it. A good operator can use it to make just the results you wish, for a permanent has many more facets than probably you realize. One facet is, of course, the most familiar one of making curls and waves in straight hair. These might be crisp, springy ones, if that is your wish, or soft, loose ones if you prefer. Another kind of permanent, a body permanent, is most popular today and its prime purpose is to add body, not curl, to your hair. It is the basis of your style, and once your style has been set, the extra lift and control that the permanent has contributed insures the set's lasting much longer. This is the hidden permanent, the permanent that you don't see. And then there's still another facet to permanents—they can even be used to straighten too-curly hair (see *Curly hair*, Chapter XII).

What makes the difference in what a permanent does and in how well it does it, is customizing—fitting the process to the hair and the results desired. But in order to understand the customizing, you should first understand how any permanent works.

Here, in brief, is how a permanent—whether it's a salon or a home job—works. Hair is saturated with a chemical solution that temporarily softens the structure of the individual hair strands, making them receptive to change. While the strand is in the pliable, receptive condition, the hair is rolled or wound into the desired shape, and kept that way for long enough to form the strands into that shape. Then the action of the first solution is stopped with the action of a neutralizer. Today's neutralizing solutions are formulated with a variety of things in addition to the basic chemical that fixes the hair strands in the desired position. It is the neutralizer that can contain humectants (for more lustrous waves), special ingredients for the protection of tinted hair, or specific chemicals for resistant hair.

It is at this point that the same principle works for straightening too-curly hair. The solution is used to change the structure of the hair. Then the hair is combed straight, kept with the solution on it for some time, then locked into straight position by the neutralizer. The process, however, is not ad-

vised for home doing; it should be done only by an expert—
since timing and technique are of the essence.

As for "customizing" the permanent, this is done in many
ways. Its tightness or looseness can vary, depending on three
factors: the strength of the solution used, the size of the
rollers used, and the length of time the solution is left on the
hair. And all of these factors can be changed for the permanent desired. A body permanent, for example—which is
the "invisible" one—will use large rollers and a short processing time, because the goal is to add only body to the hair—
to give the hair foundation for settings, to add fullness, lift,
or mass where needed for a style—without adding curls.

But other factors also enter in the final results. How the
hair grows is an important one. On most heads the hair at the
front has the most curl, that at the back the least. Therefore,
most operators start applying the solution to and rolling the
curls at the nape section first, to allow it longer processing
time. The curlier front hair will come last, for least processing
time, or, if a smooth-front style is wanted, may not be given
curl at all. If, however, your head is one of the few with its
most curly sections elsewhere, the technique should be re-
versed.

Another important factor to be considered is the condition of the hair itself. If hair has been bleached or colored,
abused, or previously permanented, it requires a special treatment. Usually, this will include a special conditioning before the permanent is given, a special kind of solution, extra
care in wrapping the rollers to avoid any tension, perhaps
using cotton wool around the ends to protect them. And hair
that has been streaked, tipped, or frosted provides its own
set of special problems, for there are now two different kinds
of hair structures with which to deal, requiring two different

types of processing—one for the natural-color hair, one for the lightened.

For some heads, some styles, a "half permanent" might be given (also called a "partial permanent"). This is not to be confused with the "touch-up" or "midway" permanent—one given to short ends between permanents. (This type is usually not recommended, because it is virtually impossible to avoid giving at least part of the hair a double permanent later—not a good idea in any circumstances.) The half permanent is one given only to part of the hair. It may be only in back, if the front hair is naturally curly. Perhaps it will be given only in front, if a special style calls for body curls there; perhaps at the crown, to lift the hair there, give it more body for pouffier hairdos. This permanent depends on skill in sectioning and analyzing the hair, to determine which should and which should not be included in the permanent.

With these variables, you can see why some permanents go wrong—why some seem not to take and others seem to take too much. Usually it's because the permanent has not been custom-tailored to the head and the hair. The wrong-size rollers have been used in the wrong places. The wrong type of solution has been used. The solution has been left on too long or too short a time for that particular kind of hair. The hair that is already curly has been given too much curl, and too-straight areas not enough.

Sometimes the reason may be a lack of care in giving the permanent. Perhaps—and this is a frequent cause of frizzy hair—that old bugaboo, tension, was used in wrapping the hair, after the cold-wave solution had been applied. Or perhaps, if the wave has not taken in spots, it's because the pre-permanent shampoo was not thorough enough, and oil left in the hair resists curl.

Whatever the reason, the fault probably lies in the process

of the permanenting, not in the permanent itself. So don't blame the poor permanent; it's a friend.

A good salon permanent administered by an expert can cost $10 to $25 or more, depending on where you live. It will also take a half day in the salon, three to four times a year. If you can afford both the time and the money, it is, of course, worth it. If, on the other hand, you are a student-on-scholarship, a young wife and mother on a strict budget—the home permanent is for you.

Home-permanent kits offer detailed instructions and come in a variety wide enough to accommodate your special hair type and needs. Basically, there are two types: the rod type using plastic curlers and the pin-curl type. Use a rod type for hair that's seven inches or longer or thicker than average. The pin-curl kind is simpler but gives a looser wave and is best for very short hair. Newest kind on the market is a roller wave—one designed just for body. If you need extra rods, rollers, or pins (in addition to those provided in your kit), be sure to buy specially coated, nonmetal ones. Old-fashioned rubber-band curlers, wire rollers, leather or fiber rollers may detract from the finished wave, so don't resort to using leftovers from your setting equipment.

You will be able to select from many kinds of home permanents—for normal hair, for resistant hair, for porous, dry, tinted, brittle hair, for limp hair that needs body, or for hair that waves easily. Some kits may not specify on the package, but the directions within will vary in the timing and application of the solutions for specific kinds of hair and desired results. Study the packages, confer with your cosmetics-counter salesperson and choose a well-known brand name. Read the directions to the letter and follow them meticulously. If this is your first try with a brand other than that you've normally used (or if it's your first whirl with any home permanent), try one or two test curls before doing the whole job.

When giving yourself a home permanent, try to enlist assistance from a friend or relative to help with the difficult-to-reach parts. Aside from that suggestion, there are only a few dos and don'ts:

1. Have hair trimmed and shaped before home permanenting.

2. Start with clean hair—although a shampoo immediately before the operation is not necessary.

3. Assemble all the supplies and equipment you need before starting. You'll need comb, curlers, towels, cotton, a measuring cup, small bowl, a good mirror and a hand mirror for checking back areas, an alarm clock or timer, brush and pins, clips and/or rollers for setting after the waving's done. Large clips to hold sections of hair out of the way are helpful too.

4. Allow enough time so that you won't be interrupted in the process—two hours at the most, depending on the kind and amount of permanent waving to be done, and your own facility in winding or pin curling.

5. Never save leftover solutions and lotions for another time. Once these products are opened, exposure to air causes them to lose their strength.

How long will your permanent last (home or salon, that is)? That all depends on the kind and extent. And it depends, too, on your hair and its rate of growth. A gentle little pin-curl permanent on hair that grows at the average rate may last about two months. A whole-head permanent on plastic rod-curlers may be counted on to last about three to four months, on the average.

Before having your next permanent (or your first one, as the case may be), decide first on the style of hairdo you wish to have. Have the hair professionally cut in anticipation of the style. Then choose and have the type of permanent you will need to keep that style pretty.

CHAPTER X

Color Cues

Like a genie wisping out of his bottle-prison when the cork is removed, today's fabulous hair colors are spinning their magic over the American woman's crowning glory, making it more glorious in most cases than nature possibly could. The estimates of just how many women color their hair to-day are getting out of hand. Some reliable sources put the figure at 30 per cent of the total female population—women who have tried at least once some form of color tint, rinse, or shampoo in temporary or permanent form. Other equally sound sources flatly say one out of every two women tints her hair, while still others round it out to sixty million girls who tamper with nature's gift or goof, as the case may be. The amount we spend for coloring products and services at home or in the salon is estimated in the hundreds of millions of dollars.

Just stop and think about it. Until a little more than a decade ago, the average salon offered a choice of three colors to the fallen woman who dared. She emerged—a blinding, brassy blonde or a black-as-a-raven-forever-more brunette or a carrottop (unlike any carrot or top ever seen). Today there are enough shades and tones for a girl to change her hair color every day of the year. Present-day society realizes and accepts the fact that a "good" girl can tint her hair. She can talk about it, can proudly divulge her "formula" (like a cherished family recipe) or she can deny it and get away with it if she chooses—so natural-looking are the colors. Let's face it, the whole philosophy of hair coloring has changed!

There's good reason for the change too. Science has not only evolved subtle, natural hues, but the application of them has been simplified to an admirable degree. In addition, there's little margin for error—the color *you* want can be yours—and, used "as directed," there's no harm to the health of your hair or your scalp. Harsh, damaging, even painful bleaches are a thing of the past—along with the corrosive soaps of the ancient Teutons. Even the fake-looking solid-color "dyes" have been relegated to the kohl powders used by the early Egyptians to blacken their hair. In their place, to-day, are delicate toners which subtly shade and highlight color into the hair, just as nature does at her best. And the creamy, quick, kind-to-the-head lighteners today do the job without drying, biting, or breaking the hair.

The almost universal acceptance of hair coloring has come about for another not-to-be-overlooked reason: cost. The all-day salon jobs of just yesterday came with a high tab. Today, the hue-it-yourself products frequently cost no more than a bottle of shampoo and only a few pennies more than a good lipstick. And a salon job is little more than the price of a new bonnet.

Finally, one of the best explanations of the popularity of hair coloring is the fact that a woman may experiment, in the privacy of her home, with temporary colors—to her heart's content. If the color she chooses turns out to be wrong for her skin tones or if she dislikes it for any other reason, she may shampoo it all out and try another. The choice is up to her; she can indulge her whims and fancies—and no harm done. She can spray a tip or a streak, a little or a lot with aerosol-packaged "temporaries." She can do a whole head "out of a bottle," still temporarily. And the newest of these products are water-resistant (of considerable importance in setting your hair or if you're caught in a thunder shower), remarkably stable in color (not appreciably oxidizing or fading in strong sun), and more and more "rubproof" (less and less coating of comb and brush and crocking off on pillowcases or white blouses). In other words, hair-coloring science marches on, with American women happily joining the parade.

Despite all these easy-to-apply, quick, and effective temporary colorings that Mrs. Homemaker has at her disposal and within her budget, she still has the color-quandary problem. Perhaps because she doesn't trust her own judgment or lacks the courage of her convictions. In any case, the most often asked question (of salon operators, colorists, friends, clerks) is: "What color is best—or right—for me?" If any general, helpful answer can be given, then it could be this: Try one or two shades lighter than the natural color of your hair. They are more flattering for all ages, and particularly for older women. If hair is graying, and the desire is its original color, then it should be darker than, say, the pale blonde or "towhead" of childhood.

Lighter or darker, hair-color selection depends on skin tones, and the correct choice can do wonders for under-par complexions, in addition to intensifying eye coloring to a brand-new loveliness. A good general guide is: For *very light, nearly white skin,* choose the champagne, ash, honey, or strawberry blonde, or golden red, chestnut, dark brown, or black; for *creamier skin,* the ash blonde, copper, light or dark auburn, chestnut, or black; for *pink-and-white skin,* all of the colors the nearly white skin can take plus copper, light or dark auburn, and all shades of brown or black; for *sallow, in-between skin,* champagne, ash, or honey blonde, strawberry blonde, red, copper, light or dark red-brown, chestnut, or medium brown; for *high-color, too-rosy skin,* reddish-blonde or brown, medium brown or medium ash blonde; and for *olive skin,* a "drabbed" ash blonde, all shades of brown, black, or auburn.

In addition to all the beauty-out-of-a-bottle that hair coloring bestows on complexions, it can also serve to correct facial faults. Experts in the salons call it "color-shaping" when they tone hair lighter at the sides to make a narrow face seem wider or darken to make a too-wide face slimmer in appearance. Too-prominent noses, too-high or too-low foreheads can be "illusioned" into more pleasing scale with color-shaping. But this can only be done by experts—just as any other tricky coloring job should be. Stripping, lightening, permanent tinting, frosting, streaking—should all be handled by trained professionals and are rarely successful as home jobs.

The biggest news in hair coloring is, of course, the "natural" look of it all. And this is achieved by softer, *toned* rather than *flat* color. The brassy, blowtorch look has gone with the twenties and thirties. And the product that achieves this does so by "drabbing" the hair or chasing the red tones out of blonde or black hair (actually dark brown hair which looks black). Salons today do not color hair all of a solid single color. They shade it, carefully, artistically—and thereby achieve the "natural" look, for natural hair is not a solid, single color—it is many shades, gradations, and tones. And it is "natural" hair that science is reproducing now—synthetically.

Whether your next color job (or the first one) is done at home or in a salon, these rules should be observed: Always read the directions carefully and know the product to be used; choose colors from a chart a shade lighter than the color desired for the hair on your head (unless hair is totally white to begin with); and have a patch test for any possible allergy before *each* coloring job.

What's a patch test? What's drabbing? What's temporary, permanent, stripping, lightening? Here's a glossary of hair-coloring terms, the special language of hair coloring you'll need to know if this is your first fling with color for your hair:

Allergy test: Test performed in advance to determine possible hypersensitive (allergic) reaction to certain coloring substances; made on a small patch of clear skin. Also called patch test or skin test.

Applicator bottle: Small plastic bottle with cap ending in slim nozzle, especially suited to applying coloring material to parted-off sections of hair; usually holds about two liquid ounces; is often marked for fractional measuring.

Ash: Having pale or cool (as opposed to warm or bright) tones; as "ash blonde" or "ash brown."

Bleach: To lighten hair by removing pigmentation; also a lightening agent.

Blend: To combine ingredients or preparations so as to achieve an integrated mixture; also, the mixture itself. The word "blending" is used also to describe the process of evening color throughout a strand of hair.

Brassy: Containing excessive amounts of red-gold or brass tone; may describe reds or blondes.

Coating: A method of coloring hair. Temporary rinses, color crayons, and sprays all color hair by coating it. Coating color remains on the cuticle or outer surface of the hair shaft, as opposed to a penetrating color (which see).

Color shampoo: Shampoo designed to add highlights and enrich natural color of hair subtly, as well as cleanse the hair; term sometimes used for shampoo tint (which see).

Color test: A test performed on the hair prior to coloring it, in which a strand is treated with the proposed formula in order to determine suitable formula and timing.

Colorfast shampoo: Simply a mild shampoo especially formulated for cleansing and protecting the color stability of hair that has been tinted or lightened.

Colorist: A qualified hairdresser especially skilled in and specializing in the application of hair colorings, the design and execution of color effects, and the care of hair that has been colored.

Concentrate: Any preparation intended to be diluted (usually with water) before use.

Condition: To improve and enhance the texture and appearance of hair by imparting luster, softness, pliability; often done before or during coloring.

Cortex: The second layer of a hair shaft, containing the pigment that gives the hair its natural color.

Demarcation line: Visible boundary between colored (or lightened) hair and natural-color new growth.

Developer: An agent (for example, peroxide) that reacts chemically with a coloring material or lightener to produce a change in hair color.

Drab: To remove or diminish warm tones (too-bright red or brassy yellow), usually while tinting or lightening. Also "drabbing."

Drabber: The agent used to diminish or remove warm tones.

Dye: Preparation in little use now that permanently coats the hair shaft with color—often artificial looking. Erroneously used as synonymous with "tint" (which see). Refer to "penetrating color" and "tint" for current methods of permanent hair coloring.

Filler: A preparation for hair which is too porous. A filler corrects overporosity; permits more uniform results in tinting or toning.

Frost: To lighten small strands of hair throughout the head, giving a misty, frosted look. Also called "frosting."

Gray: When occurring naturally, an illusory shade resulting from the combination of white (unpigmented) hairs with those of natural hue.

Henna: Plant-extract dye preparation, in little use today, that coats the hair shaft with a permanent often unnaturally-bright shade of red. Refer to "penetrating" and "tint" for up-to-date methods for obtaining red hair. So-called *white henna* is not henna, but magnesium carbonate, a harsh and highly alkaline bleaching agent, damaging to the hair. In little use today.

Highlight: To devise light-catching facets by slight lightening or toning of the natural hair.

Lift: To lighten by a barely perceptible amount, without definite color change.

Lighten: To make hair paler or lighter by removing pigment. Lightening and bleaching are the same process. The more up-to-date word is "lighten."

Lightener: Chemical agent for lightening, often incorporating conditioning substances as well as the lightening agent.

Long-lasting rinse: Semipermanent color (which see).

Metallic salts: Chemical residue left on the hair by certain temporary colors; may impair results of subsequent coloring and of permanent waving.

Overlap: Accidental retinting (or relightening) of previously colored (or lightened) hair during retouching.

Oxidation: The development of a color via chemical union of oxygen with the coloring material; also, unwanted change of a tint in the hair due to atmospheric action on it.

THE TIMELESS CLASSIC

This simplest of hairdos is never out of fashion, brushes out from the easiest of settings (see next page), and suits many faces. It's also adaptable to women of all ages. Styled by Michel of Paris, it is shown in a variety of brush-outs on the next two pages, with directions.

Photographs on this page and the next two by Gerry Low.
Copyright Dell Publishing Co., Inc., 1963, 1964.

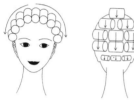

VARIATIONS ON A CLASSIC COIF

A simple, blunt cut at chin length is Michel of Paris' way with this versatile hairdo. Then set as shown in the diagrams at left on very large rollers (more for body than for curl). Wind rollers in the direction of the arrows, using smaller ones in back at the nape line. To brush out: Brush all hair back from face first, then sweep forward at sides in the line you prefer. On the preceding page: Part on either side, brush smoothly down from part, off brow, and curl guiches forward. Above, left: Lift hair with rattail comb to crisscross part as shown. Above, right: Lift center section at brow, push back and fasten with bobby pins or barrette. Curl ends up and lightly spray to hold in place. Left: A variation of right, above, with a flower-and-bow anchor and ends left free to curl forward on back of hairdo.

THREE MORE FROM A BASIC SET

From the same cut, same setting as on the preceding pages, these variations are possible. Top, left: Brush top hair straight back from forehead and catch at crown with bobby pins or barrette. Brush sides down and back from face, curling up over hand in back. Anchor with bobby pins and spray entire hairdo lightly to hold in place. Tuck daisies on bobby pins in place as shown. Top, right: Here the hair is brushed down from a short center part and flipped up lightly all the way around. With a rattail comb, lift back crown for height. Spray lightly and lift again. Left: Here the hairdo is crowned with a hairpiece for formal occasions. This is a sophisticated style, eminently suited to the mature woman as well as to younger faces. All the hair is brushed up from the face, back from the brow and fastened at top with cross-laced bobby or hairpins. Push hair forward towards face for the soft bumper effect. Fasten hairpiece on top, and add a jeweled clip if desired.

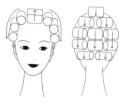
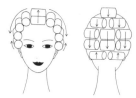

SPECIAL OCCASION HAIRDOS

Master coiffeur Michel Kazan likes symmetry in this seemingly complicated style. Hair has been cut to mid-cheek length. The setting is all on jumbo rollers wound as shown in the diagrams. After hair has been brushed out and the lines thoroughly blended with the brush, a narrow band of hair at the front center is sleeked straight back. Then the rest of the crown hair is picked up at one side and brushed high in an arch. Sides are brushed down and under and curved and lifted forward.

Anthos creates a beguiling updo here with medium-long hair. Again, the set is done with jumbo rollers, for body and curve more than for curl. To brush out properly: Brush hair back from brow, up from nape, and up at the front sides. To style: Brush center brow back to crown and fasten with bobby pins. Brush back up high and curl forward over center crown. Anchor with pins. Brush sides up and fasten at center crown over all other fastenings. Spray lightly, lift top as needed, and place jewel or bow at center as shown.

Photograph by Gerry Low.

STEP-BY-STEP TO CLIP CURLS AND ROLLERS

Photographs by Martin Iger

WAYS OF PARTING

The part you part in setting need not follow the one that's part of your finished hairdo. Sometimes, indeed, it's best to take a tack you'll later obscure in brush-out, to prevent utter flatness on either side of the part. Here, a diagonal side parting (1), Julius Caruso's own trick of zigzag parting (2), an angled parting for rolling (3).

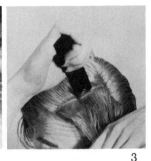

1   2   3

SETTING SECTIONS

Partings (2) and (3) are ways to separate the strands you'll wrap around a single roller. Another is to lift with finger or rattail comb making the parting purposely uneven. (Straight lines can cause brush-out breaks.) Hold straight up from head, comb other hair away (4).

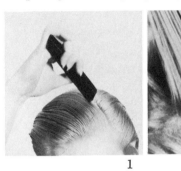

THE WINDUP

Once you've separated the section for rolling (4), hold it straight up, slanted slightly away from the direction in which you'll roll, and grasp the ends firmly (5). Place roller behind strand with other hand. As you start to wind (6), make sure ends are wrapped smoothly around roller. Ready to clip, do needed smoothing with comb (7).

4

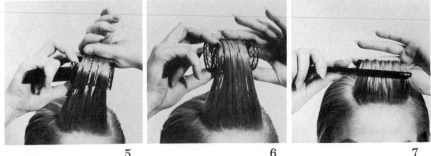

5   6   7

MAKE A TWOSOME

If your pattern calls for parallel rollers, here's the way to hold them firmly, encourage better final blending, use fewer clips too! Secure first one with clips. Clip second to first at one side (8), dispense with clip holding first (9). Same on other side (10). Two clips hold both (11).

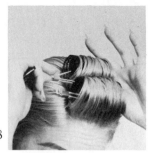

8

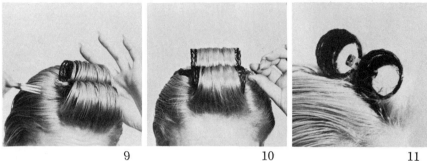

9   10   11

HAPPY-ENDING AIDS

If ends just won't wrap smoothly round the roller, you'll find end papers invaluable. They're extra-thin tissue, don't hamper drying; some come with built-in setting booster activated by wet-hair contact. Wrap around strand below ends (12), then slide to ends and wind (13, 14, 15), holding paper till ends are wound under. Then clip (16).

12   13

14   15   16

PICK YOUR ROLLER

A small, short roller can be firmly secured, with nary a mark, by using one of the new, plastic gadgets called "picks," that resemble outsize straight pins. Roll firmly in the usual way (17). Then hold in place with one hand, place pick right through curl to other side (18).

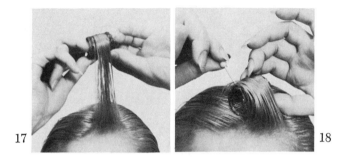

17   18

FLUFF STUFF

Where you want neither buoyant fullness nor close-clinging waves, but simply soft fluffing, try the stand-up pin curl. Its basic shape is that of a rollered strand, but the curve is more relaxed, held less rigidly. Use index finger as a "roller"; place it halfway (19), wind upper half around finger (20, 21). Then, holding curl flat, roll down to sit on head (22, 23).

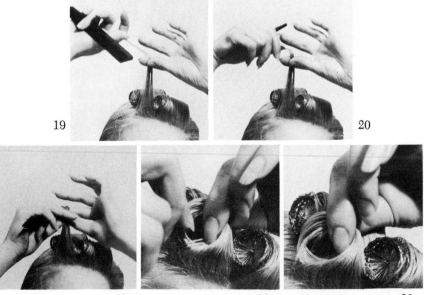

19   20

21   22   23

The stand-up pin curl securely clipped (24, 25), now notice the roller just behind it; it's different from the ones we used on the preceding pages. These mesh rollers incorporate tiny brushes (like bottle brushes) inside, with bristles that project just a bit through the mesh. Object: extra control as you roll. Best fastening: a pick.

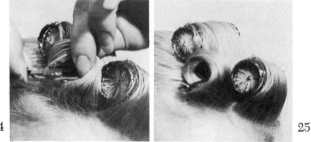

24   25

CURVES AHEAD

The coy cheek curl's best done this way for fine-to-medium hair (for coarser hair, use the method below). First, swing a ribbon of hair around index finger (26); then, curve the end of the strand in to meet the middle (27). Lay flat, pin (28). Note well position of clip and open center of the curl.

26   NAPE: CURLS . . . 27   28

The chic, softly clinging nape line can be done two ways; try both, see which is better for you. Left, the pin-curl way to set curls that lie quietly and closely. Hair length must be right, of course. First twist strand around rattail comb (29); then curve ends in and under (30), pin (31).

29   30   31

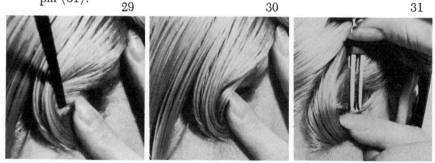

FOR TEENS, THE SHORT AND THE LONG

Here, mid-length locks are styled by Richard Gega with bangs and top-knot for a simple page-boy do. For setting directions and more teen styles, turn the page.

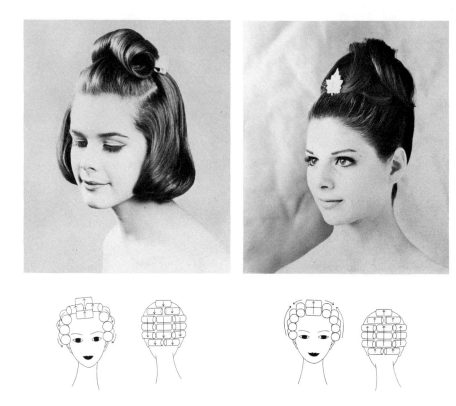

TEEN CLASSICS, DOWN AND UP

R. Keith styles this topknotted page boy for hair slightly longer than that on the preceding page, but the setting's the same. Set with jumbo rollers on the sides and medium rollers everywhere else. Follow the arrows for direction of winding rollers. Brush out straight back from the brow and down at the sides. Curve ends under and roll crown hair forward as shown (or backward as on the preceding page, if preferred). Tie topknot with narrow ribbon and spray sides and top curl very lightly to keep smooth.

Photograph by Arnold & Wolf

Richard Gega creates the simplest of updos for long hair this way. Set the front and crown on jumbo rollers and the back on large or medium-sized ones, all wound in the directions of the arrows as shown. Brush out in the same direction as set, blending all lines together in firm, upward strokes. Use a coated-elastic band designed for ponytails and fasten all hair at top crown. Brush ends up and let fall in gentle curves all around. Use rattail comb to separate curls. Spray gently to keep wisps under control.

Photograph by Charles Varon

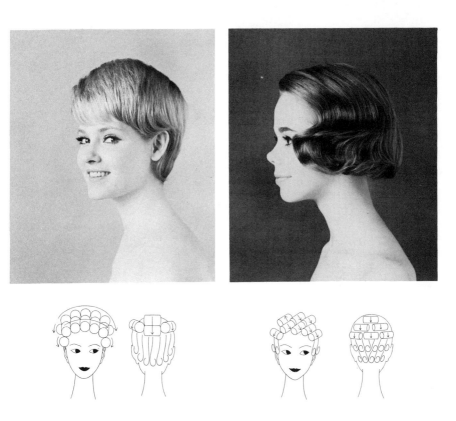

SHORT, SWEET, AND YOUNG

Artfully cut by Richard Gega, this brief cap of a coif appears to be all bangs. To keep it neatly curving and head-hugging, set it as shown in the diagram. Use large rollers and clip curls at the nape, curving in the directions shown. Brush out with firm strokes—in the same direction as the setting. Brush bangs on the diagonal, to one side, and curve hair behind ears. Spray very lightly to control wisps.

Another sweet, short style by Richard Gega, artfully cut and set to hug the head. Follow the diagram directions precisely, noting especially the direction of the clip curls designed to form the deep single wave. Brush out from a low side part (whichever side you prefer), and push wave in place with fingers to look like photograph. Spray lightly all over, and cup wave with hands after spraying to insure head hugging.

Photographs by Charles Varon

THE SILKY LOOK—FOUR WAYS

Busy young American women like best a setting that can be brushed out
many different ways. Here, George Michael of Penthouse Hairstylists
shows four styles from one basic setting design. On the opposite page,
top left: Classic, simple brush-out is parted low on one side and sleekly
brushed forward on the opposite side. Top, right, opposite: A flick of
the brush sends this hairdo winging out, wider, perkier. On this page,
above: Left, all silk and satin in a lovely version of the page boy with
hair curved under all around and one little curl winging out at the cheek
line. Right, a partless, artless little coif is brushed straight back from the
brow and swirled smoothly on the bias at back.

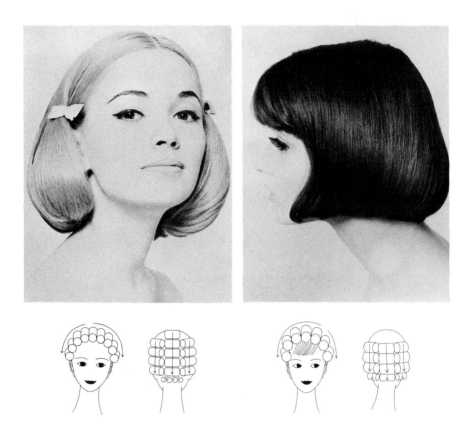

THE CLASSIC BLONDE, THE CLASSIC BRUNETTE

Two utterly simple styles that are perennially in fashion depend here on hair that has true body—achieved by nature or acquired through the body permanent. On the left, George Michael of Penthouse Hairstylists sets the hair on very large rollers as diagramed with just a few clip curls at the nape ends. The brush-out from a center part is sleekly, firmly down, and ends are brushed under all around. On the right, from Charles Coiffures is this carefully calculated bob, blunt-cut, with a thick crop of bangs. Follow the diagram to set and brush out in the direction of the arrows. Comb bangs straight or slanty.

BRIEF, BREEZY AND BEAUTIFUL

For the woman or girl who likes a short, easy-to-care-for coif here are two styles from Charles Coiffures. At the left, hair is just grazing the ear lobes. Its setting is a large-roller one and classic in placement. To brush out: Sweep all hair back from the brow and, with or without parting, curve hair to one side, forward, pushing in waves as illustrated. At the right: Briefer still and more casual, this little cap cut features brow-grazing bangs. Note carefully the placement and direction of rollers here to achieve this artfully tousled do. Brush out in the direction of the rollers, lift curls with rattail comb as desired.

Right photograph by Chaz. Copyright Dell Publishing Co., Inc., 1964.

PRETTY FOR GRAY, PRETTY FOR BLONDE, PRETTY FOR ALL

Julius Caruso creates this hairdo to show off the gleam of silvery or blonde highlights in hair. But the line is just as pretty for the brunette or redhead. The setting is on medium rollers with clip curls at the nape. To brush out: Sweep hair back and up from the face, up from the back. Fasten a wide, flexible comb at the crown, and brush back ends forward in a loose roll.

Photographs by Philip Pegler. Copyright Dell Publishing Co., Inc., 1964.

Diagrams in this section by Winifred Greene.
Copyright Dell Publishing Co., Inc., 1960, 1961, 1962, 1963, 1964.

Patch test: Allergy test (which see).

Penetrating color: Color that enters the cortex or second layer of the hair shaft to effect a change in pigmentation, as opposed to coating color. *Penetration* is the current, up-to-date, most widely used method of coloring hair permanently.

Pepper-and-salt: A term used to describe hair that has a mixture of white and pigmented strands (usually very dark brunette).

Permanent color: Color that neither shampoos out nor diminishes over a period of time but remains until hair grows out. It is a penetrating color (which see).

Peroxide: Short for hydrogen peroxide, one of the chemical agents used in lightening hair.

Pigment: Coloring matter, natural or otherwise.

Porosity: The degree to which hair is able to absorb moisture or liquid preparations.

Powder bleach: An extremely strong, fast-acting bleach used professionally under certain conditions.

Prebleach: To prelighten (which see).

Prelighten: To lighten or bleach in preparation for a second coloring procedure; purpose is usually to increase porosity for ready acceptance of tint or to achieve additional lightening for blonde toning.

Presoften: To prelighten for the specific purpose of increasing porosity.

Remover: Professional preparation which removes ("strips") permanent artificial color from hair for new coloring or lightening processes.

Resistant: Describes hair that does not accept color easily, often because of low porosity.

Retouch: To color or bleach new growth on tinted or lightened hair; also, the process of so doing.

Rinse (semipermanent): A hair-coloring preparation that imparts neither lasting color nor color that can be removed instantly by shampooing; a semipermanent rinse adds color that fades or diminishes gradually over a period of weeks. Sometimes referred to as color "lotion" or "tone."

Rinse (temporary): A preparation applied to hair after shampooing to add gloss or color; referred to as "temporary" because color is deposited on the outside of the hair shaft and can be removed (immediately) by washing with shampoo.

Roots: In tinted or lightened hair, new growth showing the natural color.

Semipermanent color: See *Rinse* (*semipermanent*).

Shade: A color; also, in commercial literature, a subtle, nearly imperceptible gradation of color (as, "will lighten three shades").

Shampoo tint: A tint (which see) applied like a shampoo and containing cleansing ingredients as well as coloring materials.

Shampoo for colored hair: A shampoo which leaves artificially tinted hair colorfast. See *Colorfast shampoo.*

Skin test: Allergy test (which see).

Strand test: Color test (which see).

Strand: Small section of hair—at least forty hairs.

Streak: To lighten a small group of strands, usually at the hairline; also, the effect so achieved.

Strip: To remove artificial color from the hair. Often a corrective procedure; not to be confused with bleach or lighten.

Temporary color: Any nonpermanent color; now used exclusively to denote color that may be removed from the hair by simple shampooing.

Tint: A preparation that colors hair permanently by penetrating the hair shaft and chemically altering the pigmentation of the cortex. The color obtained by tinting cannot be shampooed out; it remains until the hair grows out—or until it is chemically removed. Often designated in trade names simply as "hair color."

Tip: To lighten the ends of selected strands in a chosen area throughout the head of hair, to contrast subtly or strongly with darker hair.

Tone: Color quality or value—for example, a warm "tone" of brown; also, a color that modifies a hue—for example, black hair with an over-all "tone" of red.

Toner: A gentle, extra-delicate tint, applied after extreme prelightening to create any of several fashionable blonde or red shades; also sometimes used synonymously with semi-permanent color.

Touch-up: Retouch (which see).

Vegetable color: Temporary coating color using pigments derived from plants.

Virgin hair: Hair not containing, internally or externally, any lighteners or artificial coloring materials; hair that has never been altered by bleaching or tinting.

Warm: Of a hair color, containing red or gold tones.

White henna: A preparation, little used now, for bleaching. Strongly alkaline; extremely harsh on hair.

SPECIAL TIPS FOR SPECIAL TYPES

The Brownette

More than likely you *are* a brownette, because more women are that, naturally, than any other type. Many brownettes think of themselves as brunettes (which really includes only very dark brown or black hair colors); or they think of themselves as blondes because that's the color they grew up with and now it's darkened to light brown. A brownette, strictly speaking, is too dark to be a blonde, too light to be a brunette, and not red enough to be a redhead. There are, of course, many different kinds of brownettes. There's the pale brownette with fair skin (which probably tends to freckle in the sun), eyes probably blue, or maybe green or gray, and hair that's a warm brown, perhaps with red highlights. Then there's the warm brownette, whose skin is creamier, who tends to tan easily, and whose eyes are brown, hazel, possibly green or blue. Then there's the darker brownette, the one with olive skin, eyes probably brown, although they could be hazel or green. Her hair is not dark enough to be brunette, and it very likely is warmed with red highlights so that it seems lighter. The goal of most brownettes is to add sparkle, to play up the tones and shades that are present in brown hair, and, in fact, to make minks out of what some might call mice.

It seems that half the hair cosmetics industry is at work trying to perk up the brownette, and they've come up with some very good solutions. First and foremost is color—not color to change nature, but color to make the most of nature. There's much to explore: shades to produce gold or red lights; shades to deepen or to lighten; shades to mask out gray hairs that mar the brown color; and ways to streak gray or any lighter shade into brown color for exciting effects. Furthermore, these colors and shades come in many forms. There are rinses to apply after or during shampoo and wash out with the next shampoo (a good way to find which color will do the most for the hair). Then there are the semipermanent rinses that last for several weeks, won't rub off, save work and time, and are a good way of applying color—at home or at the salon—once a favorite becoming one has been found. Finally, there is the permanent toning, again to be done at home or at the salon, and again not to change the brown color, but to play it up, add life and sparkle. Many of these contain special conditioners so that the hair gets new sheen from their use as well as new highlights and color. The brownette has a wider choice of color variation than any other shade of hair and can go gradually and subtly from this in-between shade to very light or very dark attractively and with ease.

The Blonde

A blonde by birth or a blonde by election, the woman who has blonde hair needs to give it more care than probably any other color, except, perhaps gray. Everyday dirt from the atmosphere plays havoc with pale locks, so frequent shampoos are mandatory for the blonde. Sometimes, depending on geographical location, shampooing may be necessary as often as every three days. If hair is blonde-by-choice, it should be treated to a shampoo especially designed for lightened and tinted hair.

If hair is lightened it needs special enriching cream rinses, special conditioners to keep it from becoming dry and brittle. And hair spray specially formulated for lightened hair should be used to protect the delicate tone, keep the sheen natural looking.

Because sun and the very air around it can change the color of lightened hair, it should be protected from the ravages of both. Parasols, wide-brimmed hats—at the very least, scarves—should be used to protect lightened locks against the intense rays of the sun. (Smart blondes-by-choice keep a lock of their hair in a dressing table drawer to check possible changes in color.) Natural as well as other blondes need rinses now and then to keep the shade of blonde desired. And that old bugaboo of blondes—brassiness—is almost a thing of the past with the wonderful "drabbing" rinses that are so easily applied after each shampoo.

It goes without saying that the woman who has decided to become a blonde and stay a blonde will never show her head in public with so much as a millimeter of dark new growth visible. Artful toning, growing ever more creative, has done much to prolong the time between touch-ups—but touch-ups there must be. Regularly, religiously. Depending on the growth rate of the individual hair, the blonde must have her hair retouched every four weeks, and for some it may be oftener.

There's nothing in the world so drab as a pale, washed-out blonde, but on the other hand, the aureole of light that can play around a face framed in lightened hair can be extremely beautiful. To get the most out of your blondeness—if this is your category—be sure that yours is the right shade for you. Even if you're a born blonde, have a consultation with a good hairdresser-colorist to check the shade. Perhaps just a little toner, ever so subtle, may be the difference for you between being just another blonde and a more exciting one.

The Brunette

Maybe nature made your hair a deep, dark brown, or a rarer "coal black." Or maybe you helped nature along by darkening your color. However you've come by your brunette tresses, you have your own very special set of problems.

You're in good company, you brunettes, for some of the most exciting women ever have shared your dark hair coloring. No reason you can't join their company. The idea is to play up the brunette in you—don't hide it. Put away those blonde and redhead notions—and think brunette.

There's no one brunette type. There are as many as there are brunettes, but, for the sake of delineating the many facets of brunette excitement, we can group them roughly according to skin coloring, eye color, and personality. There is, to start, the sultry brunette of intrigue- and spy-drama fame; her skin is probably on the olive side, her eyes dark and smoldering, her hair close to jet black. Then there's the equally intriguing, but not so smoldering, brunette of the fair skin, the blue eyes—the Irish beauty type of brunette. Next we have the golden girl of the brunettes—the outdoor lass with tanned (perhaps even freckled) skin, the more brown than black hair (perhaps with a reddish glow to it), and eyes brown, green or blue. And we have the gamin brunette—she of the pixie features, the young (no matter her age) ways—with hair dark brown or nearly black, eyes any shade (but always lively), skin from fair to olive.

Whatever your brunette type, never forget this for a moment: Your hair, because of its dark shade, is probably the most outstanding thing about you. It's a bold, dark mass, an eye-attracting object whose shape and condition is always on display. Don't ever let just any style do; take into consideration your face shape, your height, when you consult your stylist about a new hairdo. Its silhouette is extremely important.

Your hair's color, too, is important. If you find it is fading, that it seems to be losing life, see what a temporary rinse can do to perk it up. If it's turning gray, the light streaks can be very attractive, even dramatic (that's one advantage you have over your fair-haired friends). You might encourage the look by having a few extra streaks lightened. On the other hand, if the new gray hairs only dull the whole look of your hair, don't hesitate to cover them. You'll find many fine and effective gray-covering toners available today.

And no matter whether you do or don't color your hair, don't ever neglect its condition. Your effectiveness as an exciting brunette depends on your hair's gloss, its sheen, its life. Use a conditioner if it's dry; use a remedy—and fast—if dandruff is dulling it. And always, always use your brush faithfully, to do its work in bringing out the necessary lights and to keep your hair from being a dull, flat, dark mass.

The Redhead

Red, the richest of all hair hues, is not a single shade, but several. It spans a spectrum from the nearly blonde to the nearly brown. Take the natural red-hair range. Add to those the reds that can be reached by simple lightening of naturally warm-tone (or red-containing) browns. Then multiply that figure, in turn, by the number of tints and tonings devised by modern cosmetics science to modify the spectrum.

Complexion shade and eye color may vary, too, making that many more combinations that might define a particular redhead's own color scheme. While skin tones don't cover the wide possibilities of, say, brunettes, redhead complexions can range from paler-than-pale to fresh and freckled. As for eye colors—there are no limits.

Your first step is to type yourself, determining—very generally, of course—just which kind of redhead you are.

The so-called strawberry blonde's red hair is full of golden highlights; her skin coloring is usually that of a dark blonde, typically (though not always) unfreckled. Her eyes are usually light, as often gray or green as blue. The "carrottop" nickname often goes to the girl whose hair is a light, bright red; her complexion is often quite pale, sometimes tending to a pinkish tone; her eyes are usually blue, sometimes green. A vivid, intense hue marks the coppery redhead. And the fourth type, finally, covers the range from deep auburn to a nearly brown mahogany. Complexion tones in these last two types may vary from pale-with-freckles to creamy-pale to an "average" medium tone; and it is with these deeper shades that brown eyes, fairly rare in natural redheads, occasionally do occur.

If you're not a redhead now but are considering becoming one: a note of caution for you. The rest of your natural coloring should fall into one of the schemes outlined. If you frame a deep olive complexion with auburn tresses, even nonexperts will know it's not your natural hair color.

To be a more radiant redhead, you'll have to keep that flame bright. Never permit it to pale, to lose its luster. Effective care starts with daily watchfulness. And, of course, that means: a brushing session nightly to keep those strands burnished and gleaming. If ends tend to dryness, add a little cream hairdressing (applied with your finger tips). Guard both the condition and coppery brilliance of your tresses by protecting them from the unkind elements: frizz-making drizzle, drying winds, color-damaging sun (even more important if you're a self-made redhead). Necessary items in your hair-care closet: hats, sunshades, wet-weather cover-ups, hair spray incorporating protective ingredients.

At shampoo time, use a gentle emollient kind, one that lubricates as it lathers, cleanses without removing natural oils. If hair's been toned or lightened, be sure to use one of the safe-for-you, color-protecting shampoos.

Final special note for the redhead who finds color fading a bit with the years: Avoid too-dark tints that may age you; a rinse of gold is your best restorative.

Gray or White Hair
See the special chapter for you (Chapter XVI) for special advice.

You may find—most women do—that your gray hair has, astonishingly, exhibited a whole new assortment of characteristics. Your brown or blonde hair may have been oily, thick, fine; your gray hair may be dry, thin, coarse, and willfully stubborn.

Happily, there are ways and ways to deal with this new head of hair you seem to have acquired. Dry, strawlike hair for instance, is one of the most easily solved problems these days. All sorts of hairdressings and conditioners are available, both to buy at your cosmetics counter and to be applied by your hairdresser.

And it's your hairdresser, too, who can best effect proper coiffure control for you. He can shape your hair with an eye to its new texture, its growing directions—and can plan special permanents to give it good body (without old-fashioned tightness and frizz). If thinning hair is a problem for you, your salon can probably provide a selection of hairpieces and help you plan your hairdo around one.

At home, of course, you'll follow your lifelong routine of scrupulous cleanliness, careful combing, daily brushing to keep the silver polished and to keep it truly glorious.

The Art of Lightening

The special art of lightening hair is best left to the expert colorist, as we have said. The question is: should you or shouldn't you? You *should* if: you know all the facts (you'll find many of the pertinent ones right here); you've given careful thought to your new look; you'll look and feel prettier; you're willing to learn a new set of hair-care lessons. If you've neither patience nor liking for extra care—you *shouldn't*. Not sure? Read on!

Start with some simple arithmetic . . . and you'll begin to realize what lightening can and can't do. Lightening lightens; it's as simple as that. Unlike tinting, toning, or rinsing—

which add color—lightening subtracts color from your hair.
The new shade will be merely a paler version of the natural
one, with the same tonal spectrum. A dark reddish brown,
for instance, will lighten to a light reddish brown—not to a
golden brown (some new lighteners now incorporate a special tone-changing agent—more of that later). Slight lightening's effect: a sunny glow. Selected-strand lightening may
also be recommended by a salon for the flattering purpose of
special face-shape correction; lights and shadows create new
contours that are often more complimentary. But lightening
is frequently a first step, and here's why. The lightener's
bleaching action affects the pigment cells in the hair's cortex,
or second layer; they are lightened by oxidation. At the
same time, its penetrating action makes the hair more porous,
more receptive to other preparations. Brief lightening, then,
may be used to presoften hair in preparation for tinting. And,
if the new tint is to be markedly lighter than your natural
shade, prelightening is a requisite, especially if the new hue
will have a different cast or tone. But there's another, infi-
nitely exciting fact: today, extensive lightening can give you
a whole new world of hair color. Best of all, it's a world of
hair colors you can vary at will!

Look to the rainbow, and then some: Those are all the
shades your hair can be, once it's radically lightened (and
if your hair is pale blonde or pure white to start with—there's
no lightening needed). The tint of your choice can be yours
with no fuss, whatever the nuances of your natural shade,
when the original color, complete with its overtones, has been
removed. You can even decide on no permanent tint at all,
but simply give in to your whims and change the shade of
your tresses with color rinses, shampoos, and sprays. These
remain for a week or three or eight through one or several
shampoos, depending on the product you choose. Available

now: every natural-look color you can imagine, plus a host of fantastic just-for-fun shades from brilliants to delicate pastels. Sound tempting? Your lightening, however, must be carefully planned.

Take a sample stroke of lightening, and try it on for "size." One way is a spray-on streak, near your face. Best way: a hairpiece in your hoped-for color; these are available, for just this purpose, in many salons. Your looking should be done in daylight, if possible; northern exposure will give the truest view. Next best light is incandescent—never fluorescent, which might lend a misleading cool tone. A salon visit, in fact, is a good first step whether you'll have-done or do-yourself; any good salon will be happy to talk it over with you at no cost whatever—and it's best to have a professional colorist analyze your hair shade. A "pro" can tell you what natural tones are present, what procedure is necessary for the degree of lightening you're contemplating, and precisely what the salon cost (including touch-ups) would be. Any colorist will also confirm these notes of caution: No lightening should be done if you've any problem-scalp condition or injury; lightening should not take place within a week of a permanent; pale blonding isn't usually recommended for black or deep brown hair. The last is possible now, but it's lengthy and fairly expensive.

There are some dos and several don'ts if you'll do your lightening at home. Let's take the latter first. Don't try to whip up home-brewed peroxide bleaches; they won't do the job efficiently and can leave your hair in less than lovely shape. Don't, by the same token, use so-called "white henna"—actually a highly alkaline magnesium compound that can damage your hair and scalp severely. Don't (unless you're unusually deft) attempt extreme lightening or tricky blonde toning. Do buy one of the new creamy conditioning lighteners by a reputable maker (the ones that are advertised nationally with well-known brand names). Do read the manufacturer's instructions carefully and follow them precisely. Be sure you have all the materials specified. If other preparations are recommended in combination with the lightener, use only those by the same maker. Perhaps most important, be sure that all suggested testing is carried out to the letter; this includes a prelightening test for hypersensitivity (test made on the skin), timing tests for color (we suggest a start-to-finish test on a snipped-off strand). If your hair does have a distinct red, orange, or brassy cast and your aim is pure, pale blonde, you'll find the lighteners with "blue" in their names have the greatest drabbing effect (meaning not "dulling," but red-removing). Do, finally, go slowly and beware of too much, too soon. You can always lighten further—but overbleached hair becomes harsh, coarse, and brittle, is fragile, and may be subject to breakage.

Platinum, silver, honey, pearl, and champagne are just some of the chic kinds of blonde you can be, courtesy of the special, extra-delicate tints called toners. These, because of their subtlety and delicacy, are best planned for and applied by a professional colorist. Each requires a specific degree of lightening; all require removal of red tones. Hair lightened to the stage technically described as "gold," for instance, can be toned to strawberry blonde or honey beige; ash or champagne blonding requires further lightening, and silver or platinum toning still more. The salon colorist can also achieve many special effects far too intricate for self-doing. One is the "sun-streaked" blonde-on-blonde effect for which two closely harmonized toners are used; after the lighter is applied, thirty to forty-five selected strands are specially shielded while the darker one is applied to create the "shadow" areas. Another dimension-illusion is done by the selective application of quick-acting super-bleaches in certain areas. Most complex achievement of custom salon artistry: the canny duplication of nature's own subtle deepening of color over the head, from forehead to nape of neck. A switch to a new beauty program will be in store for your newly lightened looks. First, of course, your make-up scheme will change to complement the new, softer shade. Your new cosmetics colors will depend in part on your skin tone. In general, however, if you've changed to brownette, the scheme will be softened; if you've lightened to red or auburn, you'll be using warmer tones; if you've become a blonde, the new cue will be a paler spectrum. Your hair itself, because lightening does make it more delicate, needs special care now. Use mild shampoos; look for rinses, waving lotions, hairdressings, and sprays that say "special for bleached or tinted hair." Sunbathing should include a complete cover-up for your hair, and chlorinated swimming pools should be avoided entirely. Touch-ups? Depends on the degree of lightening. Wisest way is to space them as widely as you can, and use rinses, crayons, sprays to cover new growth between real retouches.

CHAPTER XI

Wigs, Switches, and Hairpieces

No longer a fad or a high-fashion fantasy for the privileged few, the wig and the hairpiece are here to stay. Always a lifesaver for the man or woman with thinning or "problem" hair, the wig (or hairpiece) now has a place in every smartly groomed woman's fashion-accessory wardrobe. Its versatility and its practicality are attested to by the busy career girl who cannot afford to spend so many hours at the hairdresser's. Young people in the performing arts find it a "must," and frequently own several wigs as well as hairpieces. The perfection of manufacturing techniques has made the moderately priced wig and hairpiece available to more women than ever—at hairdressing salons across the country, in specialty shops, and through mail-order catalogues.

You may buy everything from just a cluster of curls, a fringe of bangs or a streak or two to a luxurious long-hair switch that may be coiled and curled to your fancy's or fashion's delight. You may have a full wig, demi-wig (or wiglet), a halo or circlet of hair to match or contrast with your own hair. The hair may be tinted any color you wish—including wild fantasy colors. You may have real hair, synthetic hair that looks real—or a combination of both. Your wig or hairpiece may be machine- or handmade. You may have a tower or a close little cap of a hairdo. And the styling of your wig can be as varied as the art of your hairdresser.

If you're wondering what kind of a wig to buy—or how to

cope with the one you already own, here are answers to the most frequently asked questions about wigs, construction, cost, and maintenance.

What are the fibers used in making wigs?

Not all wigs are made of genuine hair. Some are pure synthetic fiber (for example, Dynel); some are a blend of synthetic and human or animal hair. Some are pure animal hair (for example, yak hair); some are animal-human hair blends. If a wig is advertised or labeled as "genuine hair" or "natural hair," it is indeed that, but not necessarily pure human hair or so-called "virgin hair" (hair neither tinted nor bleached). Much of the hair used in wigs in the United States comes from Italy, France, and Germany as well as from China.

Why is there such a wide range in the costs of wigs, and is there really a difference between one costing about $50 and another that might be $300?

The difference is a matter of both hair quality and actual construction. Low-cost wigs are machine-made; the best and most expensive are handmade. The finest quality human hair, used in handmade wigs, is imported from Europe. Most machine-made wigs use human or animal hair imported from the Orient, Africa, and South America. The expensive wig is softer, finer-textured hair with luster and sheen. High-fashion-shade virgin blonde hair is the costliest.

How can you distinguish between a machine-made wig and a handmade one, and why is the handmade one usually considered the better buy?

Handmade wigs are constructed on a fine silk base or foundation with strands knotted by hand and as closely spaced as hair on your own head. Construction is done by highly skilled European-trained wigmakers and takes four to five days minimum. Fifteen machine-made wigs can be made in one day and these are made on a coarse net foundation. The hair is sewn on strips like fringe, and the strips are machine-stitched round and round with wide spaces between. The custom handmade wig will last longer and looks like your own hair, fooling the eye completely. To know what you're buying, turn the wig inside out and examine.

Why is it that some wigs fit so much better than others, and can any actually be made to stay on when worn in the wind or participating in active sports?
Cheaper wigs are fitted by measuring just one dimension of the head—much as you'd be measured for a hat. Custommade wigs are measured and fitted to five critical areas of the head: front to back, nape, headline, hairline, and side to side. The latter, properly fitted, will stay put whatever your activity.

If a wig gets bald spots or is damaged by loss of hair, can it be repaired or restored in any way?
A handmade wig—known in the trade as a "ventilated" wig —can have strands matched and replaced by hand. Machine-made wigs are almost impossible to repair because replacement of areas would necessitate ripping the wig apart and starting construction all over—at a cost almost as high as the original wig.

Is it possible to wash a hair wig, and, if so, what kind of shampoo is best to keep it looking like new?
Under no circumstances should you wash a hair wig. Either take it to your hairdresser to be cleaned, or, if you must do it yourself, use cleaning fluid (carbon tetrachloride). Do be sure to follow manufacturer's precautions printed on container of cleanser, and air the wig thoroughly—away from heat—as it is drying. Cleaning your wig in any other way can damage it seriously, loosening knotted strands, causing hair loss, and destroying its luster. Synthetic wigs may be sham-

pooed with mild detergents and rinsed in clear, lukewarm water.

When a new styling or set is desired, what special equipment is needed, and can this be done at home?

Women who are skilled in setting their own hair can indeed reset a wig. Most important to remember—don't saturate or dampen the foundation of a wig with setting lotions. Most stylists lightly dampen ends, reset with rollers or clips in the usual way. Then brush out and fix in place with a light, non-lacquer hair spray. Cutting, trimming, shaping, restyling are best left to a professional, however, just as with your own hair. Never use a wave lotion. One section of hair at a time may be dampened with water on the ends. Be very careful—don't get the "roots" wet. While you're setting any hairpiece, you'll need a firm support for it. A dummy head or block is used by professionals and one of these is, of course, ideal for dressing a whole wig. A rolled-up towel can serve as a reasonably good substitute. Ponytails, chignons, braids, et al., may be pinned securely to a wide ribbon or tape which has been looped and tied to your bathroom towel rod. The top of a bang or small switch may be placed in a drawer which is then closed firmly to anchor it as you set it. A friend or patient husband could hold the top of the piece as you braid or coil it.

To dress a coiled chignon: Twist the length of hair with the right hand as left hand holds and smooths the strands; as right hand reaches end or tail and continues to twist, the left hand starts to wind coiled portion into round cartwheel; ends are twisted, tucked under, and securely pinned on under side for a smooth finish. Plaiting a chignon-braid is as simple as braiding yarn or making pigtails.

Wigs and hairpieces may be set exactly as you would your own hair—with clips and rollers in pin curls and big, fat sausage curls. Allow the same amount of time for the new hairdo to set as you would for your own hair if the fashion hairpiece is made of real hair. Synthetic ones take less time, may be spray-curled even more quickly.

Can a wig be given a home permanent?
Wigs should never be permanent waved—at home or in a salon. The solutions would loosen strands and probably damage the hair permanently. Professionals often use an electric curling iron set at warm or very low heat.

How much does it cost to have a wig reset or styled?
The cost, as with any other hairdressing service, varies with the salon and with the geographical location of the salon. On the whole, however, the cost for cleaning, trimming, setting is slightly higher than the cost for such service to your own hair. A complete restyling is comparably higher. On an average, cleaning and resetting costs about $10. Cleaning alone may cost $5.00 and styling and cleaning of cheaper wigs (which disintegrate more quickly) may cost more than the better custom-made ones.

How often must a wig be cleaned, set, and/or styled?
This depends on the individual, how often she wears her wig, under what circumstances, and in what geographical area (in a sooty city, obviously, cleaning would necessarily be more frequent). On the average, however, if a wig is worn every day—and placed on a wig block between wearings—cleaning once a month is recommended. A casual style under such circumstances would need resetting every sixth or eighth time the wig is worn. Restyling is a matter of individual preference. A wig's set will last longer than a woman's own set, since it is usually removed and placed on its block at night instead of being worn to bed.

Can a wig be tinted or bleached if a woman decides she'd like to change the color of it, and, if so, how?

Hair wigs usually should not be tinted and should never be bleached. Some careful artisans have been able to alter color slightly, have given light—temporary—pastel tints to pale blonde wigs (these may be rinsed out and changed, say, from pink to blue to lavender, etc.). Synthetic-fiber wigs may be tinted but may not emerge looking as new and fresh as when first purchased. No wig can ever be bleached without some damage to its texture and construction.

How long will a wig last, or what is its average life?
Inexpensive synthetic or machine-made wigs last, on the average, from six months to a year. Custom handmade wigs may last from three to four years. This applies, of course, to wigs given normal, reasonable care and average number of wearings.

Must a bleached, high-fashion-tinted wig be covered up outdoors in the sun? Can the sun change its color?
Hair wigs should be treated just as you treat your own hair—if yours is bleached, you cover it. If the wig is bleached, protect it against strong sunlight, since the wig's tint can oxidize and fade or become brassy just as your own hair hue, natural or otherwise, can.

Is the quality of a brunette wig finer than a blonde one, or is any one hair shade better than another?
The finest-textured hair is virgin (i.e., unbleached and un-tinted) blonde hair. However, some natural or virgin brown hair wigs might be finer than bleached-blonde ones, since the latter have started as darker colors. The shade of hair chosen for a wig should first of all be becoming in color to the individual. Quality, sheen, texture, and workmanship should also be checked before you purchase a wig.

Can rain ruin a wig, and is moisture harmful to it?
Moisture, in general, is not good for a wig. A little, for setting

purposes, is all right, but care must be exercised that the foundation of the wig is not dampened repeatedly. Getting caught in a rainstorm is not the best thing for a wig. The same care should be given a well-set and -groomed wig that is given to your own hair when it's been newly coifed. Always carry a little plastic rain hood.

How should a wig be stored when it is not in use? Is a block necessary, and is a balsa-wood one the best?

When it is not being worn, a wig should be placed on a wig block. Blocks are made of various materials—wood (balsa is the lightest-weight), plastic, wire mesh. Any of these is good, but the lighter the weight, the easier it is to transport the wig when you are traveling. The wig should also be kept covered to protect it against dust. On its block, it may be stored in a box or in one of the wig cases made for this purpose. You should also try to have a wig block that is your own head size—neither too small nor too large for your wig —so it will keep its shape when it is not being worn.

If a dark brunette chooses to wear a light blonde wig, how can she keep her own hair from showing around the edges?

A properly fitted wig will cover the hairline completely so that there is no danger of peep-through of darker or unmatched hair. Before putting on a wig, the individual's own hair should be securely snugged to the head with bobby pins or with a nylon stocking cap that pulls hair close to the head. Special attention should be paid to the front hairline and nape hair in back if the wig is a very short style. Any stray hairs on the wearer's own head may be tucked in with a rattail comb after the wig is in place.

If a wig is trimmed for one specific hairdo, can it be styled any other way without its being reshaped or retrimmed?

Just as your own haircut can be set in many different ways, so can a well-shaped wig be reset and recoiffed in a variety of styles.

How much hair spray should be used on a wig?
No more than you would use on your own hair. Most important, of course, is to use a hair spray or light fixative that contains no lacquer.

May a home hair dryer be used on a wig after setting?
Yes, but just as when setting your own hair and drying it with a home hair dryer, carefully cover the set with a fine net to keep it tidy as the air circulates over it. Place the wig on the block, place the dryer hood over the wig, and dry with the thermostat set at either "cool" or "warm," never "hot."

Is it possible to have a switch made from your own hair?
Hairpiece manufacturers recommend that you query them first before having your hair cut. Length of hair for a switch should be a minimum of twelve inches, weigh at least eight ounces. It should be of top quality—not overbleached, dried out, or full of broken ends and split hairs. The only acceptable hair for purposes of selling it is that which has never been tinted or bleached. The best long tress may net you no more than $5.00.

Should wigs or hairpieces be given conditioning treatments?
If you're dry cleaning your own, remember that this process removes all the oil, as well as the dirt. Ends, especially, become dry. Rub conditioner into them gently with your finger tips. There is a special reconditioner for wigs, and it's a good idea to use it whenever the hair looks dull or dry.

Will wearing a wig hurt your own hair?
If you take proper care of your own hair, it should stay

healthy even if you frequently wear a wig. Today's wigs are lightweight and may be readily cleaned; and the "ventilation" or porousness of the base allows your own scalp to breathe normally.

Can a wig be "teased" or back-combed?

Synthetic-fiber wigs and hairpieces should never be teased, because the hair will loosen and fall out. Even a real hair wig (as well as your own hair) will suffer damage from violent, excessive back-combing.

Is brushing bad for a wig or hairpiece?

Quite the contrary. Insufficient brushing can cause matting in the fine-mesh base with the result that hair loss will be greater than when the hair is brushed frequently to keep the tresses unsnarled.

Can a wig stretch or shrink, and if so, can this be corrected?

Perspiration can cause the wig foundation to shrink, and keeping it on a block that is too large can cause it to stretch. Your hairdresser may correct this by dampening the net foundation and placing the wig on a correctly sized block overnight. For bigger alterations, the wigmaker or hairdresser may take quarter-inch tucks in the foundation.

What is the proper way to put on a wig?

Your hairdresser will show you: Hold wig by side flaps and lower wig forward over brow, adjusting from front to back— never from back to front.

THE VERSATILE SWITCH

Below is a simple, lightweight, eleven-inch switch and with it five examples of formal and informal arrangements on medium-length hair:

In this gala treatment, one half of the hairpiece is pulled across the front, over the forehead, while the other half becomes topknot curls. An ornament can cover the cross-over.

Here the switch makes a dip to the side, over the ear. The other side can be flat. Bangs are your own—brushed down and under, to the side, blending in deceptively with the switch.

When is a ponytail not a ponytail? When it's a switch. Here it's doubled over and attached at the cross-over with a pin or decorative clip, then hangs down, curling naturally.

Smooth look for short hair comes with the hairpiece used this way. It's centered in back, then swoops frontward on both sides, over ears in a sleek swirl that hides the short ends.

How about a classic knot? This daytime one is a little to one side. It's the switch, of course, tied in a knot, then pinned on securely to the pulled-back hair for this so-charming effect.

Drawings in this chapter by Winifred Greene.
© Dell Publishing Co., Inc., 1960.

CHAPTER XII

Problem Hair

Sooner or later everyone has a hairdo problem. Yours may be acquired—or you may have been born with it. In either case, there are extremely few hairdo problems that can't be solved, compromised, or compensated for. Some you can cure yourself with common sense and sound hair care. Some may need the assistance of a good hair stylist, one who has a thorough background in modern cosmetology. Some very serious problems—excessive falling of hair, scalp disorders, obvious diseases—will need the advice and help of a physician, even a specialist like a dermatologist. Below, in alphabetical order for convenient reference, are the most common hairdo problems among women today—with suggestions for solving or compensating for them:

Allergies: Frequently a problem that affects scalp and hair care, allergies should be treated by a physician. If you're prone to allergic reactions, be specially careful when you try any new hair product. Read labels carefully. Follow directions to the letter. Always make a patch test before using sprays, treatment shampoos, or hair-coloring products.

Baldness: Hair loss is measurably increasing among women, and any one of several causes are known. The abnormal loss of hair (*not* the normal rate of about eighty hairs per day in a healthy scalp) is medically termed *alopecia*, and there are five major types of it: (1) *Male-pattern baldness* characterized by a receding hairline and thinning crown with the eventual meeting of the two areas is permanent. There is, to date, no known way of preventing or retarding it, and it is hereditary. So-called "cures" for this type of baldness, according to all reliable medical authorities, are simply hoaxes. In most instances of such claims, the baldness stemmed from some temporary condition and spontaneous growth is offered as evidence of the "cure." (2) *Post-infectious alopecia* can happen to men, women, and children. It may occur anywhere from eight to twelve weeks after an illness (usually an infectious disease accompanied by high fever, such as typhoid or influenza), and is generally temporary. Increased temporary hair loss following pregnancy is included in this category. Usually there is an early return of normal hair growth. (3) *Senile baldness* is not true baldness, since late in life the scalp, like the rest of the body, ages. Production of new hair slows down, and as hairs are lost in the normal process, they are not replaced in such quantity. Hence, the hair becomes sparser. Again, heredity is the dictator here. (4) *Alopecia areata* or *patchy baldness* may occur in either sex at any age. Hair loss is in localized patches of varying sizes and shapes and may occur gradually or literally overnight. One cause of patchy baldness may be physical—pulling out or destruction of hair. Too-tight ponytails, the wrong kind of hairbrush, severe stretching on hair rollers might cause bald patches at the hairline. Another theoretical cause: emotional disturbance, sudden or continuing to a degree to impair physical health. Medical treatment is indicated, and prognosis is most hopeful when the condition has not persisted for a long time. Regrowth of hair after patchy baldness is usually in the form of down like an infant's, followed by normal-textured but unpigmented hair, and finally, hair of natural color. (5) *Female alopecia diffusa* is characterized by gradual, nonlocalized hair loss

—a widening of the part is noticeable, with "show-through" of the scalp and increasing numbers of hairs lost in brushing. The same causes as those for patchy baldness are attributed here with diet deficiency or glandular imbalance also playing a part. Whatever type of abnormal loss of hair you might be suffering, the important thing is *first*, see your doctor. Meanwhile, of course, clever hairdoing and styling, a chic wig or hairpiece can camouflage the condition until it can be arrested or cured, if possible.

Body: Lack of body once was the bane of many women who yearned for a luxurious, bouncy hairdo. Today, clever cutting (see Chapter XVII), special permanents that add "body" without visible curl, setting lotions with built-in assists of body-building—all help to give otherwise unmanageable, bodiless hair bounce and workability. Hair coloring, too, changes the elasticity of hair, often makes it more controllable. Ill health, of course, can be the reason for your bounceless, bodiless hair. Check your diet. Better yet, check with your doctor and find out if your physical condition is up to snuff. Other health rules to observe if you would have healthy hair: enough exercise, adequate sleep—lack of which can contribute to lifeless, unmanageable hair. Watch your basic hair care program: daily brushing to perk up scalp circulation, give airiness to your hair, and distribute natural oils evenly. Shampoo with one of the protein preparations made specifically for body-boosting; follow with a cream rinse to tame your locks into submission. Many of the suggestions for baby-fine hair (see *Fine hair*) control will help here too.

Brassiness: The bane of the blonde, the redhead, and the sun-worshiper, brassiness, an orange, egg-yellow cast to the hair, can be muted and toned. Whether you're a blonde or redhead by nature or by choice, those harsh, brassy highlights can be modified. The simplest way is to rinse your hair with a drabber (a temporary rinse that does not dull but tones down undesirable harsh yellow or brass color). Most corrective drabbers are in liquid form in blue, purple, slate, or silver color, and on the container label will be a phrase like "for white, gray, or bleached hair." These drabbers are temporary, may be washed out easily, and, in some cases, have shampoo action as well. Most are used after hair has been shampooed and rinsed with clear, warm water. Then the hair is lightly towel-dried for a minute but left quite damp. The drabbing agent is usually mixed with warm water in proportions specified in the directions, then applied evenly to the damp hair. To insure even distribution, comb it through the hair as quickly as possible. Then set as usual. Many drabbers have built-in conditioners. If the amount and proportions specified are not enough to cut down on the brass in your hair, try a little more of the agent next time with less water—if the instructions indicate that this is permissible.

Broken ends: Chances are that hair with abnormally split ends is excessively dry, hence brittle and subject to breakage. First, replace the oil necessary to supple, flexible hair. Conditioning treatments, a change of shampoo (to one that includes emollients—labeled "for dry hair"), cream rinses after shampooing, and diligent brushing to distribute existing natural oils. Too frequent, too harsh bleaching can cause split ends. So, too, can overpermanenting with the wrong solutions for your hair type. And overteasing or back-combing, worn-out rollers, jagged-edged clips, hair wound too tightly in settings—all these factors can contribute to broken and split hair. Have the ends trimmed—never singed—and start a routine of sensible hair care at once to restore sheen and shine to your abused locks. Several professional reconditioning treatments may be necessary.

Climate: Where you live, geographically, can have a damaging effect on your hair if you do not take precautions against the atmosphere and the climate. Needless to say, if you live in a sooty, industrial city, frequent shampooing is essential to the health of your hair. A tropical climate or one where fog and dampness prevail make humidity a special foe of certain kinds of hair. Extra-curly hair and overbleached hair will absorb the moisture and make hair unattractively frizzy-looking. Use a protective, anti-humidity spray before you go out. Works, too, for hair that goes limp in moist atmospheres. Hot, dry climates demand that you brush your hair more often than if you lived in a moist climate. And conditioners to offset the drying-out of your hair should be used regularly—before, not after the damage is done. Wear a hat or scarf in any case—to protect your hair from the hot sun or the dews and damps. A cold climate presents other problems: static electricity (see *Electricity*) and the steam heat of homes in cold areas of the country. The latter has the same drying effect as the sun and the treatment and prevention are the same to keep hair lustrous and healthy: faithful brushing, conditioners, hair sprays with built-in conditioners, and cream rinses to restore shine and sheen.

Coarse hair: Usually the healthiest hair, but often maddeningly unmanageable, coarse hair may also be bushy and wiry in texture. A special cut by a good hair stylist can tame this type of hair. Extra-strength hair spray helps control waywardness. Cream rinses will help to make it soft and flexible. Curly, wiry, coarse hair may need professional straightening (see *Curly hair*) to bring it under control. Brushing, as always, helps here.

Cowlicks: Styling is the answer to stubborn cowlicks and a clever hairdresser—or clever you—can camouflage them with a hairdo that puts cowlicks to good use. A cowlick is either the beginning of a wave that stands up or the whorl of a natural curl that refuses to go in any direction but its natural bent (heredity's the culprit again!). Some hairdressers have been successful with milder cowlicks by the use of spray, barrettes, clips, and ribbons that forcefully train hair against its natural bent. Best bet, we believe, is to join it, not fight it. Have you a stubborn cowlick right in front? Then part your hair diagonally across the crown and swoop bangs or a band of hair down from it. A crown cowlick? Try a pouf over that. A lower side part, a swirled back springing from the cowlick, a high, rounded coif—these are but a few of the styling tricks that can use, not oppose a cowlick.

Curly hair: No problem this, unless hair is too curly. If all professional help—the right cut, the proper setting on extra-large rollers, controlling hair sprays, conditioners, and taming hairdressings—fails and hair is still too curly, then have it straightened professionally. Do not attempt hair-straightening at home. The process, in the hands of a professional, will not hurt your hair—it is actually a permanent wave in reverse, using, in essence, the same solutions that are used in permanent waving.

Dandruff: Not all "little white flakes" on the collar are true dandruff. A certain amount of dead-cell shedding is normal. But scaling off of the scalp at an excessive rate is not. Many medical specialists relate the condition of dandruff to the malfunction of the oil glands at the roots of the hair. Others attribute it to metabolic disturbance. Poor circulation, improper diet, inadequate cleansing, harsh detergents, toxic hair preparations, bacteria, sex hormones, fungi, "nerves"—all have been blamed as the cause of dandruff. Simple dandruff can be of a dry or oily variety. The dry type presents itself with dry, hard, white or gray flakes. The oily type is characterized by yellow, greasy, often crusty flakes, and the hair itself frequently feels oily as well. How can you control it? By maintaining scrupulous cleanliness—frequent shampooing, brushing before and after washing the hair, using clean tools (brushes, combs, setting implements), rinsing hair two and three times after shampooing, and changing pillowcases and towels oftener than usual. "Dandruff remover" shampoos help (though they won't cure), as do medicated lotions or rinses applied either immediately before or after shampooing. Follow the manufacturer's directions carefully; some mild cases of dandruff may, in time, be alleviated and can often be eliminated for a period of several months. If the tendency exists, dandruff may return—but using rinses, at longer intervals, has been found to be effective, sometimes, in preventing recurrence. That is, in the case of simple dandruff. Yours may be more complicated. Study your scalp carefully. Look for symptoms that may accompany the little flakes, such as redness, inflammation, definitely oily patches, or cohesive clusters of flakes, bleeding, scablike crusts of any kind, or spreading of the flaking or itching from the scalp to any other area such as the forehead or ears. Any one of these indicates a condition which, whatever its cause, demands medical attention; they are symptoms of a variety of afflictions which include psoriasis (an inflammatory infection), eczema (sometimes of emotional origin), and assorted sensitivities and allergies. Do not, ever, under any circumstances attempt to treat such a condition yourself, whatever you may read about so-called "miracle" patent medicines. See your doctor immediately. Once you've eliminated the possibility of a more serious condition (your doctor will decide), you can conclude that you do, indeed, have simple dandruff. If you regularly visit a hairdresser who is familiar with scalp problems in general and yours in particular, it would then probably be wise to follow any recommendations he or she may make. But be discriminating. Treatment or advice by an incompetent beautician could make things worse. If you've followed all these precautions and self-help suggestions and still those little white flakes persist, what then? Even simple dandruff may be caused by internal factors such as diet deficiency or other apparently unrelated ailments; and only a physician is qualified to find the answer.

Dry hair: Mousy and dull, lusterless with broken ends, often frizzy and flyaway—that's dry hair. Dandruff may also be part of the picture (see *Dandruff*). Brushing, again, is necessary to stimulate the flow of natural oil along the hair strands and to the ends. A special-for-dry-hair shampoo and, after washings, special conditioning rinses or hairdressings, will help turn your hair from straw to silk again. If hair is extremely dry, an occasional hot-oil treatment will help: before your shampoo, apply warmed oil-base hair tonic through your hair; cover with a special heat cap or a towel wrung out in steaming hot water (rewet towel to keep it hot) for fifteen to twenty minutes. Then shampoo. Use a hair spray that's made for dry hair and observe simple precautions like covering hair in sun, salt water, and wind. Don't leave rollers and clips in hair overnight, but set during the day and remove implements as soon as hair is dry. When you use a hair dryer, set control for "cool," never "hot" drying. If you color your hair, take care that your salon uses the modern tints that include conditioners. Have your stylist use one of the special-formula salon permanents, if you're having a new wave, one that's specifically designed to prevent dryness and aid retention of natural oils.

Ears: Big, flyaway, or jug ears can limit your choice of hairdo, but there are many concealing styles—the classic page boy, the flip, the forward-curving bob, upsweeps with ear-covering waves—which are always in fashion. Soft poufs at the sides of your coif will easily camouflage ears that jut out.

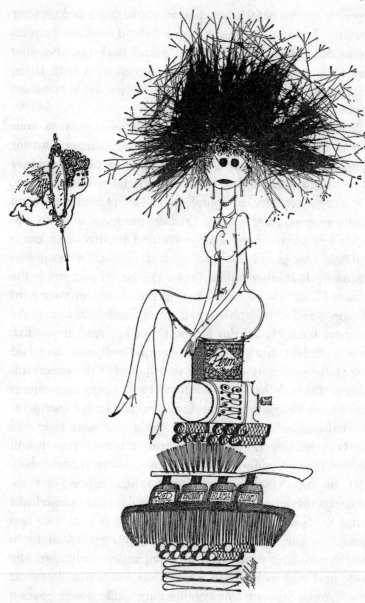

Drawing by David Silverstein.
© Dell Publishing Co., Inc., 1963.

For very special occasions, when an ear-baring hairdo is your goal, try daubing a little spirit gum behind each ear (available at drug stores) and literally "paste" back the offending ears for a few hours. Too-big ears, ornamented with large, pretty earrings, can become a plus feature on certain occasions.

Electricity: The eerie phenomenon of electricity in your hair is, for most people, a now-and-then occurrence. But for quite a number of women this recurs with such regularity as to be annoying and to present a special hairdo problem. It's static electricity, of course, and it won't hurt you—even if you're generating sparks. Friction produces it when objects of opposite charges, negative and positive—like comb and hair, plastic and wool—are rubbed together. Atmospheric electricity is another phrase for it. The air around you is the villain. Clear, dry climates step up the charge in your hair. (Foggy, smoky atmospheres and warm, humid climates make for more tractable hairdos for most people.) And, if you live on a mountain in a cold atmosphere as well, you may find that static electricity can make your hair virtually uncontrollable at times. What's the solution? Hair sprays keep things under control, to a degree, as do cream rinses after shampoos. Natural-bristle brushes will quiet flying hair more than will synthetic bristles. If electricity is truly a bother, then it will be worth your while to invest in a genuine tortoise-shell, horn, or wood comb instead of nylon, hard rubber, or steel. Less expensive but only sometimes available in oriental gift shops are bamboo combs. The best calmer is your own two hands. As one top stylist puts it: "Caress your hair for a long minute with your hands, stroking and smoothing it. The body heat and moisture of your palms will settle electrified hair." Add a plus of hair conditioning while you're getting things under control: rub your hands, brush and/or comb with a little cream hairdressing or your favorite conditioner, and stroke your hair into place.

Eyeglasses: Glasses can be a problem in planning your hairdo, but the variety of frames designed for almost any set of features makes the problem a simpler one than it was for our grandmothers. If contact lenses are not for you, be sure to choose eyeglass frames that complement your features. Here, if you can't decide what looks best on you, are some general rules: A round face usually looks best with upswept frames, wider frames slightly arched with deeper outlines. A square face becomes softer, more nearly oval in appearance with frames that sweep up and out toward the temples. The diamond face—narrow at top and at chin—achieves the oval illusion when frames are two-toned, tinted above the eyes, colorless below. The heart-shaped face—or triangle with a narrow base—avoids pixie or harlequin frames and wears an almost level top-line frame. The oblong face wears wider frames, gently arched with deeper-than-usual frame area. For most eyeglass wearers, a simple hairstyle is best, usually worn away from the face. Avoid too deep a bang, which accentuates the glasses. Choose a style that, preferably, covers the earpieces (and choose frames with slim earpieces that won't break the line of your coif).

Face shape: (See Chapter III).

Falling hair: (See *Baldness*, this chapter).

Fine hair: If it is not thin, this can be the loveliest kind of hair. But in order for it not to be flyaway hair, it will need careful cutting and cream rinses after shampooing to control it. Baby-fine hair that's too thin presents a fairly common, withal difficult, problem. It will tend to be limp, wispy, difficult to manage because of its lack of body (see *Body*, this chapter). A short, simple hairstyle is best for this type of hair—with a special taper cut in leaves and layers to create the illusion of more hair or thicker hair. If hair is oily as well as fine, then frequent (almost every day) shampoos will be necessary to keep hair from looking and feeling limp. There are special hair sprays, too, for controlling fine hair. And endpapers for roller and clip settings will help keep the wisps and flyaway ends tucked in. A good body permanent will help, too, to make the hair look and feel thicker.

Flyaway hair: (See *Fine hair* above).

Fog and hair: (See *Climate,* this chapter).

Glasses and hair: (See *Eyeglasses,* this chapter).

Gray hair: (See Chapter XVI).

Hairline problems: Brow too low? An irregular nape line that perhaps grows down too far? There are hairstyles to camouflage these natural faults, of course, and a skillful hair stylist can help you decide on the proper hairdo for your special problem. A brow line can be raised (many actresses have had this done) and a nape corrected permanently by electrolysis. This, however, should be done only by a qualified, licensed technician. If the work is extensive, it will be correspondingly expensive. Inquire about cost before you proceed.

Humidity: (See *Climate,* this chapter).

Limp hair: The problem may be "fine" hair (which see) or hair lacking "body" (which see). Investigate special setting lotions and hair sprays for hair that doesn't hold its set. Shampoos with egg or other protein may also help correct the situation.

Long hair: Not always a problem, but if hair is truly long (to the shoulders or longer), it requires special care, special handling (see Chapter XVIII).

Menstruation: (See *Nerves* below).

Nerves and hair: Tension—nervousness and anxiety—can rob hair of its natural beauty and keep it from looking its best. Hair itself does not contain nerves, but a network of nerves surrounds the openings or follicles from which hair grows. When you are tense, these nerves contract, cut off the supply of blood nourishing the hair roots. In addition, during periods of tension the glands which secrete sebum—the glands which help to make your hair glossy with the proper amount of natural oil—become overactive. Plus this: Muscles near the hair roots contract involuntarily when you experience stress or fright. No circulation, contracting muscles, too much oil—all spell disaster for your hair. You know how often your hair acts up when your menstrual period is due, or during the period itself—just a reaction to tension. The same thing can happen to your hair when you have a cold or feel out of sorts. You see the results in hair that won't stay groomed, falls limply, lacks luster, elasticity, and body. Anything that affects the elasticity of your hair affects its behavior, so very often a permanent won't "take" properly during a period of tension. It's easy to diagnose a case of "worried hair"—but it's not so easy to cure it. For thinking peaceful thoughts is easier said than done when you're under great pressure or are seriously troubled. You can, however, overcome some of the effects of tension by giving your hair extra care during these periods: get that blood circulating again by brushing your hair more. Hold your head down and brush evenly, steadily for a full ten minutes. Try massaging your scalp with the balls of your finger tips or your knuckles (never your nails), loosening the tightness of the muscles of your scalp. Anything that helps to relieve the pressure you're under—a good night's sleep, for one—will help bring the sparkle back to your hair as well as to your eyes. Don't expect overnight results if you've been living at a hectic pace and neglecting your hair for years. Faithful daily brushing and massage will improve the looks and "feel" of your hair.

Wait till it's back to its peak condition, too, before you have that next permanent.

Oily hair: Some oil is essential to healthy hair. Too much makes pretty hairdoing difficult. You'll know you've excessive oil if hair separates and looks and feels dirty and greasy the day after you've had your hair done. Like your dry-haired friend, you should check with your doctor if oiliness is way past normal. He may tell you your diet is at fault. If both your hair and skin are exceedingly oily, you'll avoid fatty foods, stick to plenty of protein, leafy vegetables, fruit, milk. Young people with oily hair often suffer from acne as well, and the fat-free diet will help complexions too. Frequent shampoos—with a detergent type formulated for oily hair—are a must. You may need daily shampoos, not only to clean the hair of oil, but to free it from the extra dust and dirt that oil attracts. Between shampoos a strict program of faithful brushing to regulate and distribute the oil will help. For days between shampoos when hair is specially oily, rub the hair before brushing and combing with a clean terry towel. The towel will remove some of the extra oil and dirt, leaving hair more manageable.

Overbleached hair: Hair that has been bleached too often, with the wrong chemicals, or hair excessively exposed to sun and salt water is hair that has been abused. It will be more porous, absorb water more quickly, and hence take longer to dry. It will look dry and dull. It may also have split ends and suffer severe breakage (see *Dry hair* and *Broken ends*, this chapter). Hair in this condition is extremely delicate. Use special shampoos and rinses for tinted and bleached hair. Avoid sun and salt water as well as swimming in chlorinated pools. Wash hair in warm, not hot water; dry hair at cool or medium temperatures, never hot. If hair is in very bad shape, take a rest from permanent coloring and try temporary rinses with built-in conditioners for a while. Follow conditioning tips for dry hair and hair with broken or split ends.

Permanent-wave damage: A rare thing today, frizziness or split ends or any other damage resulting from a permanent wave is usually attributable to human error—yours or your salon operator's. Wave solutions are so exactingly formulated that you should be able to have precisely the kind of curl you wish. If you don't, chances are somebody didn't read, and follow to the letter, the directions printed on the product package and on the accompanying instruction sheet. See Chapter IX for home and salon permanent wave details.

Pregnancy and hair: The life and luster of your hair may suffer during pregnancy and for a while after delivery—anywhere from one to several months. The hair may seem droopy, fall out at a greater than normal rate, be difficult to manage. This is a temporary situation which does not affect all mothers-to-be, and if it does occur, the best treatment is simply good, sensible care—brushing, shampooing properly and regularly, using special conditioners to help restore luster and sheen. The problem will clear up naturally in time.

Rain and hair: (See *Climate,* this chapter).

Root show-through: When this is the case and you want to let your natural color grow in after hair has been lightened, you can fool the public for a while by eliminating the part in your hair. That's the area that first shows the color contrast. Setting hair on large rollers lifts the hair up and away from the part, too—helps hide the darker-roots area. Brushing hair forward, wearing a diagonal bang—these are good camouflage tricks for the brow line for a while too. A gray-at-the-temples brunette will find one of the touch-up color crayons a tide-over till the next complete coloring job. Or a temporary rinse to match a darker, natural shade may be the answer for the dark-at-the-roots blonde who's returning to her original color. And, of course, if you can afford it, there's the nice trick of wearing a pretty, real-hair wig while your hair is growing back to natural.

Split ends: (See *Broken ends,* this chapter).

Straight hair: Depending on the whims of fashion, straight hair can be a bane or a blessing. If smooth, straight hairdos are in fashion and are becoming to you, then your problem is no great one. If wavy hair is your heart's desire, the obvious answer is a good permanent wave (see Chapter IX). Perhaps on the other hand, your hair really is not "poker straight" (a rather rare condition actually) and all it needs is a good haircut to bring out the latent curl. If you've been wearing your hair long, its weight may make it seem uncurly; a skillful haircut and a shorter hairdo may be all you need to bring out the wave that was always there.

Sunburned hair: (See *Dry hair* and *Overbleached hair,* this chapter).

Tension and hair: (See *Nerves and hair,* this chapter).

Texture: (See *Thin, Thick, Coarse, Fine,* this chapter).

Thick hair: Thick hair is usually coarse hair. If it's straight (see *Straight hair,* this chapter), a proper haircut and a good stylist are your best friends. If it's curly and coarse and thick (see *Curly hair,* this chapter), your problem is compounded, and straightening, expert cutting and pruning, diligent brushing are all "musts" for you. Cut too short, your curly, coarse hair may be too wiry and stiff for manageability. Consult a professional for the proper cut—one which will include some thinning (not with the ancient, pinking-shears type of thinner) with shaping, tapering, perhaps layering with a razor shaper. If it's straight and thick, the cut is still all-important, and you may need a light permanent wave just to tame your hairdo into shape.

Thin hair: Often thin hair is also "fine" hair (which see, this chapter) and body-building is your challenge then. You'll consult the best stylist you can find, and he or she will cut your hair to give it the illusion of thickness—trimming to a short-to-medium length, since the downward pull on longer tresses can make thin hair seem thinner. A permanent wave is a necessity—not for curl, but for body, and some prepermanent-wave conditioning may be necessary, too, since thin hair is usually fragile hair. Shampoo often; oil and dirt will rob your hair of body, drag it down, and flatten it. Set hair on really big rollers, to make it as full as possible. Use special setting lotions that can provide holding help. Brush often: for even oil distribution, for controlling, fluffing, and puffing. If you tease or back-brush to get more fullness, do it with great care in order not to damage your thin, fragile locks (see Chapter VII for brushing techniques).

Thinning hair: (See *Baldness,* this chapter).

Tired hair: Even the healthiest head of hair will react and suffer when it's overworked. Too much teasing (see Chapter VII), too much home-style bleaching (see *Overbleaching,* this chapter), too-tight roller settings left in too long, neglect of your own health, neglect of basic hair care (regular shampooing, conditioning, brushing, etc.)—these are some of the things which can contribute to "tired" hair. Whatever the cause, the symptoms are: Once your hair held its set beautifully; now it doesn't. Once it had sheen and shine; now it's dull. Once it was bouncy and springy; now it droops and it's lifeless. Perhaps you've been wearing the same style for ages? Your hair can actually become "tired" from being dressed in the same way day after day. A change of part from one side to the other may be all it needs to gain new vitality. Cutting very, very long hair may revive your tresses, giving them a chance to "breathe" in a new, shorter do. Scalp massages, a warm soak in the tub, and an all-over body massage may relax you and rejuvenate your hair (see *Nerves and hair,* this chapter). A trip to your doctor for a general health check-up and a change of diet (probably to a more sensible, more healthful) may be the simple solution to the problem of your hair looking and feeling "tired."

Water and hair: Depending on where you live, the water with which you wash your hair may be the source of trouble. If yours is a soft-water area, you have no problem: you can use either a soap or detergent-type shampoo, choosing it according to your particular type of hair. One caution: soap can be very difficult to rinse out with soft water, so be extra careful to rinse several times, getting every bit out. If you live in a hard-water area, a soap shampoo may not be enough to cut through the minerals in the water, and a dulling film can remain after your shampoo. A detergent-type will do a better job, especially if your hair is oily. If hair is dry, try a combination shampoo, one with mineral-cutting ingredients, plus a built-in conditioner to combat the water situation without robbing your hair of natural oils. Salt water—as well as chlorinated pool water—should, of course, always be rinsed thoroughly from the hair immediately after swimming. It's better not to get your hair wet when swimming, but for active swimmers and divers, this is nearly impossible. Caps with special liners and chamois headbands can help keep the hair from being soaked. Caution: Chlorinated water can affect the delicate tones of some lightened hair, causing it to turn an unattractive greenish shade. The remedy? See your colorist.

White hair: The special problems of white hair (and so-called gray hair) are handled in Chapter XVI.

Yellow streaks: (See *Brassiness,* this chapter).

CHAPTER XIII

Children's Hair Care

That beautiful head of hair every young mother envisions for her child can be a reality. Heredity will dictate color, texture, degree of waviness, cowlicks, and amount of hair, but proper diet and hair care will insure the beauty of your little girl's or boy's locks.

Naturally, your family tree (and your husband's) will determine the kind of hair your baby will have. It's true, however, that baby may be blonde, brunette, or redhead, although 85 per cent of his ancestors had hair no lighter or darker than medium brown. And true, too, that more than 50 per cent of his forebears might have had hair straight to mildly wavy, yet his may be lamb-curly. The odds depend on heredity's whims. Two things, however, you can know for sure even before baby's birth: His hair will be no darker than his darker-haired parent's; no curlier than his curlier-haired parent's.

You've heard, perhaps, that carrots can produce keen eyesight; milk builds strong bones and teeth; butter stimulates the growth of thick, curly hair. And indeed, these foods are good—for nourishing the body and insuring excellent health. However, no one food alone can make a child's bones strong, improve eyesight, or promote luxurious, wavy hair. To be sure, diet plays a large part in the health of the hair—but it is this same diet that produces a healthy child from top to toe. Therefore, be sure your child is eating a daily, well-balanced diet which includes foods from each of the four basic groups. And, as hair is nourished through blood vessels, this over-all good diet will produce a strong, shining head of hair, plus a strong, healthy body.

Your child's hair care begins in infancy. At first, it's as easy as baby's daily bath: a soft, sudsy washcloth rubbed gently over the hair and scalp, a thorough rinse with lukewarm water, and then the locks are patted dry with baby's towel. If the hair is merely a coat of down or a close little cap of fuzz, no further care is necessary until the hair becomes longer and thicker. Quite often, an infant is born with a thick thatch, even with a crop of curls. Then a few gentle strokes of a very soft baby brush (much like your own powder brush) will help to encourage hair growth as well as to bring out the natural lights and sheen of young, new hair.

Babies, too, have hair problems—the most notable being the so-called "cradle cap" which may appear over your infant's crown. This scumlike deposit on the soft spot on top of the head should present no cause for alarm, but does demand that you not try to scrub it off. A bit of baby lotion or oil gently rubbed into the area each day will speed its disappearance.

Until your child has reached toddler age, then, hair care is simply an extension of the bath, and a bar of mild castile soap does the trick. The first real shampoo may take place on or about the first birthday, and this early introduction to beauty care and cleanliness should be made as pleasant as possible. Choose a gentle shampoo, one of the special-for-children kinds that don't sting the eyes. If your little one doesn't enjoy having a wet or sudsy face, use a plastic shampoo shield (made like a hat brim with no crown) to keep hair above eye level as you lather and rinse. The bathtub is, of course, the most practical site for that first shampoo—complete with floating toys. If your child has a washable doll, you might shampoo its hair as a play demonstration. The routine is simple: First dampen the hair, then lather thoroughly, and finally rinse extra-thoroughly. A second lathering is not necessary unless you've a mud-pie artist in the family. Once a week, until adolescence, should be often enough for a shampoo, since children's hair is rarely oily.

Many fond mammas dream of a halo of golden curls for their children, but heredity is inclined to produce a minority of heads with blonde, wavy hair. If yours is a child with absolutely straight hair that seems to grow every which way, don't despair. And above all, resist the temptation to use curlers or permanent-wave solutions on your little girl too soon. Whatever kind of hair your child has inherited, your responsibility until he or she takes over her own hair care is to keep those locks clean, healthy, well-groomed. When your young lady grows up she may take advantage of the many miracles of cosmetics science to change the color or curl as she wishes—but only if you've given her a sound, healthy head of hair with which to work.

Your best ally in child hair care is the brush—applied gently, firmly, evenly. Always brush in the direction of hair growth—never against it—with a smooth, polishing action. Brush up and back, training hair to grow that way and promoting a tidy hairline for later life. Any latent curl will also be encouraged by gentle, everyday brushing.

Although grooming is more important than styling for the very young child's hair, most mothers can't resist playing hairdresser with baby's brief locks—especially if baby's a girl. If it's a boy, this is her only chance to have him look angelic. Father will step in and demand a man's haircut for his son all too soon. If you must play hairdresser, here are some ways: Gently towel-dry hair, and, while it is still damp, brush or comb (with a blunt-toothed baby comb, please) "curls" over one or two of your fingers. Hold for a second and slip fingers out. Brush end curls over fingers or the edge of your hand. No hair spray, no bobby pins, no setting tools yet! If you'd like a part on one side or the other, try to locate the natural parting area first by studying the hair when it's damp to see the natural separation spots.

Resist the temptation to trim or cut hair yourself. Haircutting, for best results, is a job for professionals only. Proper trimming of a child's hair is very important, even more so than that of grownups. Whatever tendency to curl exists is aided by skillful cutting. And poor cutting can actually destroy any natural inclination to wave. So, as soon as your child is ready for her first haircut, assign the project to the best hairdresser you can find—one who enjoys cutting children's hair. Little boys are another story, and their place is at the barber shop.

When will your child be ready for her first professional haircut? The age varies with the subject and the rate of her hair growth. Some babies may have as much hair as a three- or four-year-old. Others might have just an inch of hair right through the second year. A good rule: have it cut when it's too long. And "too long" means any amount of hair that cannot be managed, look well-groomed or is out of proportion to the child's face.

As your little girl grows, she herself will want a hairdo of her own. One of the most attractive—always neat-looking and easy to care for—is the ponytail. For variety's sake, here is a collection of very young ponytails, with drawings and directions showing how to make each style. You can vary these dos even further with ribbons, posy clips, or even a colored yarn braid or bow. Naturally, the prettiest ponytails begin with well-shampooed, well-brushed hair. To hold the various tails, use only coated-elastic bands—never the plain rubber ones—to avoid hair damage. These hold the hair firmly without pulling or tearing. When used on small sections of hair, the bands may be looped around several times until the hair is snugly secured. Be careful not to pull hair too tightly. The longer the hair, the greater number of pony styles you can create.

The Kindergarten Ponytails

The ringlet ponytail starts with two sections pulled out straight as shown, then raised high on the head and fastened together on the crown with a perky bow.

Hair here is brushed straight back on both sides so all hair is massed in the back. Then hair is brushed up from the nape and a flowered band goes on to hold it.

The Pre-teen Ponytails

The pigtail pony starts just the way a basic one does with hair brushed back from the sides, up from the nape, and fastened. Then tail is braided neatly and fastened near the end with another band. A tiny bow might be added here.

Pinwheel ponytail has a tailored look and starts with a center part. Make a ponytail about three inches above each ear; fasten tails; braid and fasten ends. Wrap each braid in a wheel and secure firmly with bobby pins or hairpins.

The Alice-in-Wonderland ponytail starts with part from top of ear across center of head to other ear. Pull the hair above part back and fasten into ponytail with a band. Drape ends over longer hair.

The bullfighter ponytail begins with a center part and a tail on either side of the head about three inches above each ear. Fasten each with ponytail band, close to the head. Roll each tail forward toward the face and brush out into smooth poufs.

The bow-tie ponytail starts with two tails: Part hair in back horizontally, from ear to ear. Use hair above part for top ponytail and remaining hair for second tail. Divide top tail in half; roll left half to left and right half to right to form two poufs. Secure with bobby pins.

The double-mane begins with a horizontal part across the back, as for the bow-tie ponytail. Gather hair above part into a ponytail and secure with a band. Form remaining hair below part into second tail to hang below first and secure. Brush out both ponytails and let hang free.

Drawings by Winifred Greene.
© Dell Publishing Co., Inc., 1960, 1961, 1962.

Movie-star hairdos are not for the very young, but your little girl may delight in wearing a style patterned after one of her favorite storybook heroines. Perhaps one of these may be just right for her type of hair and for her face:

HEIDI's hairdo depends on cut—by an expert—to bring out the curl, layer it for body, and control it for easy manageability. This shape is best for little girls (and their teen sisters too) with naturally curly hair. The pouffy crown is achieved by brushing the curls up for height. A hair ribbon with posies gives this style a party air for special occasions.

SLEEPING BEAUTY's is a long hairdo styled for a party. Draw all hair, except bangs, up toward the crown, catching with a ponytail band. Form a fat roll and secure with bobby or hairpins. Spread roll out and circle with flowers or a ribbon.

DOROTHY from the Land of Oz has a simple but charming do. Part medium or long hair straight up the center of the crown and all the way down the back; draw hair to either side and fasten with coated-elastic bands at chin level. Tie bows over the bands. Brush the feathery little bangs straight down.

RED RIDING HOOD's style is really a double ponytail. Brush hair back from bangs in front, divide it down the middle in back with a neat, straight part, and pull hair up into a high-riding ponytail above each ear. Fasten with bands and bows.

CINDERELLA's coif starts with sectioning: bangs brushed out in front; another section, about three inches wide, parted off behind the bangs part. All hair in this section is then drawn back, fastened with a coated-elastic band, to drape over the back. Side and back hair hangs straight, curled a bit on ends.

ALICE IN WONDERLAND's hairdo is a classic—the simplest of all—just drawn back, brushed shining-smooth, and caught with a snug hair ribbon or hair band. Ends may be lightly curled.

SNOW WHITE

SNOW WHITE has her hair cut shorter around her face, with the rest left longer. Hair is parted from one ear, across the crown, and to the other ear. All the long hair here is drawn back, fastened (and perhaps centered with a flower or a bow), with ends left to layer above the longer locks.

Drawings by Janet Dorchuck.
© Dell Publishing Co., Inc., 1961, 1962.

And what about little boys? To instill early habits of grooming-with-pride and to promote proper hair growth, your young man should visit the barber as soon as he can walk. Professional styling of his hair at this early age will help him to an attractive, manageable head of hair by the time he's ready to enter school.

A few preliminaries before that first trip can assist the

barber and make future sessions pleasant and comfortable for the child. Try to determine the natural bent of his hair. Dampen it with water, comb it back, and push up on all sides. You will see its natural part emerge, the line of growth, the presence of cowlicks, if any. Work with these, never against, in daily combing and brushing. A week or two before the first real haircut, have your son visit the barber to observe his father's hair being cut. Then, if possible, let father, not mother, accompany him on his own haircutting sessions.

Young boys' hair is generally cut shorter than adults', but age and taste of the individual vary this rule. The average trip to the barber is biweekly. If you live in a very small town, your selection of a barber shop may be limited. Therefore, it's advisable to know a few ground rules for your young man's haircut. Study the child's face and head shape carefully. Is it a wide, round face? Then sides should be close cut and perhaps a brush-top cut to add height will help to create the illusion of a more oval face. The longer, narrower-faced child should have more fullness at sides. A high forehead on a rectangular face is minimized by a casually brushed brow, and a chubby, square face is given more fullness at sides and an all-over rounded cut to soften the corners of a too square image. A lower side part can help the square-face picture too.

After-shampoo time is best for studying the kind of hairstyle for your little boy. Comb it, damp, several ways, and decide which is most becoming. Then give—or have your husband relay—instructions to the barber on the way you wish your son's hair cut. A good barber will listen to your wishes, will make suggestions of his own from his experience and knowledge. And a good barber will taper the hair properly—only with a razor or comb and scissors, never with clippers. Make your son's haircut a regular part of his grooming. Don't skip trips to the barber, for nothing is so untidy looking as a boy's (or a man's) hair in need of cutting. The regular, periodic visit now will automatically become a habit when he grows up.

The special problems that beset young hair now can become real bugaboos of hairdoing in adulthood. Here, then, are hints on correction and prevention of some common, as well as uncommon, child hair-care problems. Until your child is old enough to visit a hairdresser or barber, you'll be wise to begin remedies yourself.

Flyaway baby hair: Most common of hair problems in childhood is thin, baby-fine, flyaway, and/or wispy hair. Some toddlers outgrow these characteristics, but many young women (and young men) are plagued by this condition throughout their lives. Until proper trimming and shaping— and later, for young ladies, permanent waving for body—take place, the best program is a daily one of extra-diligent, gentle brushing to bring out the natural oils from the scalp along the hair strands to the very tips of the hair. Be sure, too, that your child is eating a well-balanced daily diet and check his or her general health with the doctor or pediatrician.

Poker-straight locks: For little boys, a blessing, usually, but for little girls a bane. And for the mother who dotes on curly hair, the sight of her child's board- or poker-straight hair is a frustrating one. Faithful brushing to promote sheen and luster can make even the straightest hair look attractive. A little shape and contour can be achieved by brushing the hair away from the face and up, but always in the direction of natural hair growth. Later, skillful trimming and shaping by a stylist will do wonders. Resist curling too early. Too straight hair is—in most cases—more easily remedied than too curly hair. For the miss in this plight, later, there's the miracle of permanent waving!

Bad hairlines: Is baby's hairline too low or too high or too irregular? For the time being, during babyhood, simply keep brushing the hair away from the face and up. After shampoos, towel-brush the hair as you dry it with an up-and-away stroke or tousle. Then, when it's time to visit the barber shop or salon, corrective measures may begin with an illusion-making hairstyle. A special bang for a little girl can alter the look of a too high forehead; another kind of bang can make it look higher. A curved cut for a boy can create similar illusions.

Dry, flaky scalp: Dandruff is rare among little children if a sound regimen of grooming and cleanliness has been faithfully followed. The yellowish crust on a baby's head is, as we have mentioned, the so-called "cradle cap" with which many infants are born. It will disappear and is not to be confused with dandruff. A dry, flaky scalp does not signify dandruff either. Its correction, again, is a matter of the brush and distribution of natural oils in the hair. Check the shampoo you are using, too, to be sure that it is not drying—such as one that would be used for an oily scalp condition.

Stubborn cowlicks: More often the problem of little boys than of girls who, having more hair to arrange, can camouflage with a style that counterattacks cowlicks satisfactorily. The answer to this problem is artful parting. A cowlick can be a whorl, an arc, or a concentrated growth of hair that refuses to grow in any but its own natural direction, no matter how the hair is set or combed. There is no way to fight that direction. Simply part the hair to follow the direction of the cowlick and settle for a hairstyle that conforms with its direction. Never attempt to brush or comb hair against or in the opposite direction of a cowlick.

Too thick, coarse, bushy: Some infants are born with a thick shock of coarse, bushy hair. Often this disappears during the first few months of life, and a different type replaces it. But many children grow up with hair that's heavy, coarse, far too thick. This kind of hair is among the healthiest varieties but can be difficult to manage. As soon as possible, the child with too thick hair should be taken to a stylist for a special kind of cut. Don't attempt to cut it yourself—the result could be hair that appears even thicker and bushier.

Too curly, wiry, frizzy: Heaven-sent is a child with a halo of golden ringlets. Problem-prone is the one who has too curly hair that tends to become frizzy in damp weather and turns wiry as time goes by. Resist the temptation to explore hair-straightening processes when the child is young. When she —or he—grows up, this can be done if the problem is very serious. It should be done only by a qualified professional. For the moment, keep the child's hair styled in a brief cut for a more attractive look, and, as always, practice that daily routine of brushing to counteract frizziness.

Greasy, sticky, oily: Oily hair is an extremely rare condition in the very young child, but it is quite common in adolescence. Then excessive oiliness can be a nagging problem. Too-oily hair must be washed as often as is necessary to keep it looking clean and to prevent its becoming sticky or strandy-looking. This may be as often as every third day. Under no circumstances should a shampoo with a strong degreasing property be used, as this will irritate the sebaceous glands and aggravate the existing condition.

Eyeglasses or stick-out ears: The girl who wears glasses and the little boy with a pair of jutting or flyaway ears must have hairstyles that take these problems into consideration. Your stylist or barber can create becoming hairstyles that make these problems less conspicuous. Be sure to select eyeglasses with frames that are suitable for your child's face shape and be sure to take the glasses to the salon or barber shop for try-on before each styling. Remember, too, that taping your child's ears won't correct them and will serve only to make the child self-conscious and uncomfortable.

Allergies and irritations: Scalp irritations and allergies are problems for your doctor or a specialist. Do not try home remedies, because you may unwittingly and unintentionally create an even bigger problem that could seriously endanger your child's chances for having a lovely head of hair in adulthood. Any persistent scalp sores or rashes, any balding spots or undue loss of hair should be treated only by a physician.

Finally, a word about when and how to permanent wave. Many mothers tend to give a child her first permanent at a far too early age—before the hair has fully evolved its growth pattern and developed some semblance of a style. When, then, is the best time to begin permanents? When a little girl both needs and wants one—usually a time soon after she's of school age. Perhaps her hair is so thin it's impossible to keep nicely groomed and styled, or so straight it's unmanageable. Then a permanent becomes more than just a beauty improvement; it's also a psychological lift for the growing child.

Before the permanent, if it's to be administered at home, see to it that your daughter has a good, professional hairstyling—cutting, shaping, and a hairdo that's exactly right for her. Be sure, too, that her hair is in fine, healthy condition. After these important preliminaries, select a home permanent designed specially for children's hair. Shampoo the hair thoroughly first; then follow the manufacturer's directions to the letter. Always—*always*—do one test-curl first (and before every permanent thereafter). If it's to be just a little ends-permanent, you'll find the job is simple. Or perhaps the hair requires only a light "body" permanent to give it more manageability, rather than more curl. If that's the case, read and follow the directions on the package for this specific procedure. Using the proper wave solutions on your child's hair will assure happy results without damage to those young, growing locks. One last word: always have a grown-out permanent trimmed before giving the next one.

CHAPTER XIV

Teen Hairdos and Don'ts

The biggest hairdo problem a teen-ager has is her mother. And sometimes her father or her brother. But mostly, it's Mother. Here are some of the complaints most often voiced:

"Mother won't let me use color."

"Mother says I use too much spray."

"Mother hates teasing."

"Mother (or Father) hates seeing me in rollers."

"Mother says I'm always at the hairdresser's."

Well, there are problems today for daughters—problems Mother and *her* mother never had at all. There's hair coloring, for instance. Today, many—perhaps in some areas, most —women use hair coloring of one kind or another, and their hair is more attractive for it because today's manmade color can look as good as or better than nature's own. The question is, then, how young should a girl be—or how old—to start experimenting with color? The answer: in her teens *if* the color change is neither radical nor permanent. Overbleached and dried-out brassy blonde locks, harsh orangy-reds and dull, jet-black tresses are unsightly—at any age, but even more so when worn with young, pretty faces. The trouble is, too many teens are ruining their hair when it's young and vigorous, simply because they're doing the unpardonable: cooking up home-brewed colorings or bleaches or, worse yet, using the wrong products for their hair in the wild exhilaration of experiment. Only disaster lies ahead for the girl who tries one tint on top of another and, to compound the abuse, doesn't follow directions to the letter. The results, after a short time, include such unhappy problems as split ends, broken hair shafts, frizziness, lifelessness, and a dry, strawy look over the whole head—not to mention the unattractive color that cannot be controlled. Small wonder, then, that a hairdo-knowledgeable mother becomes upset and worried about the fate of her daughter's hitherto healthy hair.

Young hair has a special quality with all the pluses of youth on its side. If it is well cared for and you are a normal, healthy teen, your hair shade is at its prettiest, most vibrant, and shining now. You say it's mousy? Well, don't experiment with permanent tints or lighteners—the results can be not only harmful and unattractive but costly—to correct and to maintain. If you enjoy experimenting with your locks—and what girl doesn't?—indulge in some harmless tricks. Get a magnifying glass, for instance, and hold a strand of your hair under it. Study it carefully, separating the hairs. See how many colors there actually are in your hair. Mousy? What's that little bit of red-gold or pale blonde or warm brown in there? Decide which you have the most of and which you'd like to have more of. Then consult the chart of a temporary hair rinse—one which lasts only from shampoo to shampoo. Follow the instructions carefully and you'll find that there are new highlights—pretty ones that accentuate your natural color, won't change it basically, and won't harm your hair. After you're, say, sixteen, you might try one of the semi-permanent tints—one with a conditioner built in. Experiment here too. Try a little on one strand near your face. Let it dry. Brush the strand wide and flat and study it against your skin tone, see how it looks with your eyes. Look at it outdoors and indoors under artificial light. Like it? Then go the whole head, but not before you're absolutely sure that it suits you.

The nice part of this kind of semipermanent tint is that you won't have to do it again for weeks and weeks, and when it grows out there won't be any contrasty roots to bother you and give your secret away. You've simply enhanced your natural color and made the most of it, and when the new growth appears, it will blend nicely. If you've been a silly girl and bleached your head to straw and brass with sun, salt water, peroxide, and ammonia, this same color conditioning can help you back to hair beauty. You can tone down the brassiness and help restore the silkiness as you grow back to your natural color.

As for streaking, frosting, tipping—that's a matter of how artfully, how subtly it's done—and a matter of age. A thirteen-year-old with blonde streaks in her brunette hair looks frankly ridiculous; a seventeen-year-old with subtle sun-blonde lights in her light brown hair can look very attractive. Again, this is not a matter of home-brewing and home-doing. If you can afford it, have a skillful beautician do this trick for you (and you must be able to afford the periodic touch-ups as well)—otherwise, be your natural self and concentrate on having shining, natural locks. Remember, you do have a decided advantage over your older sisters—and your mother —in that your hair is healthier by virtue of its youth. But to keep its youthful glow, be as careful of it as you are of your young skin.

The most common dilemma for today's teen is one of style. Mothers tend to like the plain, simple, little-girl dos; daughters frequently are in disagreement and want to try something new. Here's where compromise is called for. Of course, times have changed, and Mother may not be up on the new styles. But good taste hasn't changed, and Mother may be more aware of and more objective about what is and what isn't becoming to her daughter. Perhaps among the "modern" styles is one that is not only new—pleasing you—but also more becoming, not so exaggerated—winning Mother's okay. There are times, however, when Mother doesn't "know best." There are mothers (and even fathers) who insist on a particular hairstyle for their daughters that may be completely wrong for the girl. And they can be rather unreasonable about it. When this is the case, it's best to call in a neutral party. Both should go to a good hair stylist for a consultation on daughter's hair to get his unbiased—and expert—view on the best styles for her.

A teen should look her age, should wear styles that play up nice, healthy, shiny hair. The exaggerated, highly teased styles that parents find so much fault with are not only unbecoming but also out of fashion. As we've said in Chapter VII, there's nothing wrong with a little teasing of hair to cover a part, fill in a line; but when teasing becomes so exaggerated that parents—and even teachers—object, you must be overdoing. The same is true of hair spray—using it so excessively that hair seems plastered and untouchable, rather than soft and inviting to the touch. As for constant rollers and clips and bobby pins bristling in the hair—that's a matter of bad planning. All that paraphernalia was never meant to be seen in public, nor even in any room of your home but your own. It's rather like going to class or to dinner with cold cream all over your face. If hair needs such constant setting, there's something wrong with the cut, or the set itself; or maybe the hair needs a body permanent so that it holds its set better. Study the advice, instructions and directions in Chapters VI, IX, and XVII to help your hairdo over these hurdles.

What about salons for teen-agers? If we're talking about weekly visits, that becomes a matter of economics. Most teen girls these days are very adept at hairdoing (much more so

Chignon Ponytail—Great idea for a date, for a prom hairdo. Make
two ponytails and secure with coated-elastic bands. Divide top tail into
two and roll into poufs, one to the left and one to the right. Comb out
bottom tail and roll ends under. Fan out roll to meet the poufs of the
top ponytail.

SIDE-SADDLE PONYTAIL—This one takes a basic ponytail to the side for a very different, very sophisticated look. In this fan style, the ponytail is made at the left side of back of head and secured with a ponytail band. Comb out the tail; roll ends under to form a large roll. Hold roll in place with clip and fan out prettily in a loose effect.

FRENCH-TWIST PONYTAIL—Another lovely formal way to try. Brush all hair back very smoothly. Pick up a third of hair on left side and fasten with a coated-elastic band. Take remaining two thirds on right side, roll and twist to the left, covering first ponytail. Fasten with hairpins from nape line to top.

Drawings by Winifred Greene.
© Dell Publishing Co., Inc., 1960, 1961.

than their mothers), and they need salon visits only for hair-cutting or for very special occasions. If more frequent visits are "musts," then you should be expected to finance the visits yourself from your own allowance or earnings.

As to the style—the same rules apply for you, the teen-ager, as for your older sisters. The shape of your face, whether or not you wear glasses—these factors enter in to your choice (see Chapter III for how to find the right style). If you like brief and breezy dos, or the medium-length, flippy ones, your hair will have to be specially cut—and regularly (see Chapter XVII). If you like very long hair, that requires special care

and special handling (see some hints in Chapter XVIII).
Above are some ways with long hair, one or more of which
may be adaptable to your own locks and all of which look
prettier than long, long uncontrolled manes.

Study the hairstyles and the directions for setting them in
the picture section of this book. If you find one that you like,
that's suited to your hair type and your features, then show
the picture to your hairdresser. Remember, the proper cut is
necessary for a specific style. And the proper cut is a professional one—not an amateur snipping, razoring, or slicing done
by you or one of your friends. Only if your hair has been
shaped, cut, styled by an expert can you achieve results with
home hair setting. Check with your hairdresser, too, about the
condition and nature of your hair. If it's too fine in texture
for the style you've selected, he may recommend a special
body permanent. If it's too curly, he may suggest another
style altogether—or even recommend special hair straightening for you. Listen to him. Follow his advice if you'd avoid
disaster. And remember before you make the next wild decision to cut it or color it yourself—it takes a long time to grow
another whole hairdo. It takes, for average healthy hair,
about one whole month to grow a tiny half inch of hair!

CHAPTER XV

A Word for the Men

A woman, after a visit to her beauty shop, is certain to evoke some sort of comment from her husband (or some other male close to her—father, brother, beau)—anything from, "You look different, dear!" to, "Your hair looks marvelous!" A man, on the other hand, after a trip to his barber too often hears a rather disappointed, "Oh! You got a haircut."

But it needn't be this way at all. Not every man looks on a haircut as a necessary evil, nor on his barber as just someone who wields a fast clipper and a faster opinion on the state of the Union. There are some lucky males who have discovered that a barber can be a "beautician," a grooming authority indispensable to the preservation of their male vanity. They have found masters of the barbering craft and have discovered the pleasure and the youthful look and feeling that can come from such things as a witch-hazel steam facial, a scalp and neck massage, a cocoa-butter special, an oil treatment, a facial pack, a suntan facial, and a scientific scalp treatment. Unfortunately, this pleasure and aid is known to far too few. The fault lies partly with the shops—too few offer "complete services," and too few owners exploit the possibilities of their profession to the fullest. But mainly, the fault lies with the wives who don't care enough.

It is high time for each wife to take a good look at herself and then at her husband; time to examine her dressing table and compare its contents with the half-shelf of the medicine cabinet that houses the meager supply of her husband's grooming aids; time to compare what she spends on her looks and what her husband spends on his. And when she's done that, she can drive her husband to the door of a good barber and let him take over from there.

Statistics on record show that most men want hair-grooming preparations that will keep hair neat all day, make hair easy to groom, and keep hair from drying out. About 71 per cent of all men use some sort of grooming product. In 60 per cent of the homes the husband shops for his own hair grooming products, and in the remaining 40 per cent where the woman shops, she selects the brand. Unmanageable hair is the main reason why more than half the husbands make their very first purchase of hair-grooming products. For those women who do the buying of their husbands' grooming toiletries—a word: Be as careful in choosing these as you would your own. Is the hair dry, oily, dandruffy, fine and flyaway, too-kinky? Buy shampoos, conditioners as you would your own hair products—those that are specifically designed for specific kinds and condition of hair.

What about your gentleman's graying hair? Particularly if it's not attractive on him and makes him look as if he were aging fast? There is hair coloring, of course, and more and more men are using it. But how does a woman get a solid citizen, a conservative man, to take the daring plunge? There's a way. Each man, despite his armor of strong prejudices and the solidest of logic in argument, carries with him something that can disarm him in seconds: his vanity. His lady fair should be the first one to give vanity a nudge. She knows well that no man, and especially her own, wants to grow old. And he certainly doesn't like growing old while his wife does not. A few feminine tricks are in order here. The wife sits before a mirror with a photograph album open to their high school pictures. She calls her husband, innocently points to their pictures, and, with a look-at-us-now, has him look at their images in the mirror. This, followed with a "Someone mistook me for your daughter the other day," as fuel for the building fire, and then an "I would look as old as you if I didn't cover my gray hair" could cinch the argument. Cheating? Perhaps, but this is an extreme example, and a little feminine diplomacy usually can convince him more easily.

Some men have farsighted bosses who pick up the tab on a hair-color "lift." They rightly believe that a good company man is even better if he looks young and attractive, but has the experience of an older man. And they are knowledgeable enough to have learned that the magic of hair coloring can often turn the trick. A good barber will suggest covering up unnecessary and unattractive streaks.

Biggest bane of the male vanity is baldness. Unlike lightning, it does not strike suddenly—but like lightning, it can and does strike in the same place. For heredity is the prime culprit. If all your man's forebears were bald, chances are he will be too. If your husband is a high-strung, intellectual type working under great pressure all the time, his nerves can speed up the process. It is far easier to talk a man with a receding hairline into acquiring a hairpiece than it is one who has long become used to his baldness. In many cases, a man tends to think that his condition has not worsened with the passing years. "I've as much hair now as I did when I graduated from college" is the protest. Here, a woman's "logic" once again can come to the rescue: "But darling, you're not as young as you were then, and somehow the forehead shows more now." The message will come across.

A bit of research into the number of "wigged" celebrities and the over-all numbers of men wearing wigs or hairpieces today could help a loving wife put hair back on her husband's head. Today's experts can create hairpieces for men which are absolutely undetectable as such.

It is not false pride to tint hair or to wear a wig. A well-groomed man, an attractive, youthful-looking one gains in stature at home, in business, and especially in front of his mirror where his self-esteem is bolstered. Out of a feeling of love and pride, women can and must help their men to this so-easily acquired state.

CHAPTER XVI

How to Be Gloriously Gray

No matter what your mirror may tell you—there's no such thing as "gray" hair. It's a scientific fact: the hair on your head that gives the illusion of gray is actually white. "Gray" hair is a fool-the-eye phenomenon, just as the "blue" of the sky is an optical illusion. The color of your hair depends on the composition of your hair strands—specifically, the second layer of each hair shaft. There, many thousands of pigment granules are arranged in a unique pattern—their shading and placement (a combination of inherited factors) determine both the shade of your hair and its lightness or darkness within that shade. At some point in your life a change begins; this point may occur as early as your teens or as late as your eighties—again, principally dependent on heredity. Pigment production starts to diminish—not by sections of hair (although the process usually takes place first at the temples), but strand by strand, or even pigment cell by pigment cell. The result: not gray, but *absence of color*—white. As these white strands appear among colored ones, the shades are optically "mixed" by your eye and appear as "gray." Of course, when all the strands lose their pigmentation, you will have white hair that's visible as such.

When the first strands appear, if you're a dark brunette, your hair color may be termed "salt-and-pepper." Later, as the percentage of white or unpigmented hair increases, the color may be called "steel." Next stages: from silvery to pure

platinum white. Brunettes, as a rule, grow gray most gracefully because of the striking contrast of light and dark.
Blondes and light brownettes have the biggest problem, because the effect can be mousy, drab, often yellowish in an
unattractive way. Redheads tend to look as if they're fading
gradually and shading becomes less golden, more pinkish.

"When your hair has turned to silver," as the song goes, it
can do just that today and be the most glorious crowning
glory of your life. But it's up to you. You cannot simply sit
back and let it gray at will. You'll need a whole new outlook
on hair care, on the clothes you wear, on your make-up and
your accessories. To be elegantly, beautifully gray or snow
white does not take a great deal of money. It does, however,
take intelligence, taste, and some know-how.

You and your hairdresser will decide when and how you
should "go gray" or white. If you are in the fortunate first
category of very dark brunette, you may let nature take its
course, depending on conditioners and rinses for highlights
only to keep your hair healthy, glossy, and beautiful. If you
are a very pale blonde, your strands of white will tend to
make your hair look still lighter. Again, until more than 50
per cent of your hair has turned, you will follow the care
program of the dark brunette. After that, your hairdresser
will probably advise temporary coloring to retain your blonde
shade until all the hair is white. Brownettes and light brunettes as well as dark blondes and redheads may follow the
light blonde's way or may subscribe to permanent coloring
to cover the gradually increasing "gray" or white strands.

Once your hair is clearly and definitely "gray"—when it's
obvious to you and your friends—then comes the exciting fun
of trying the many rinses, shampoo tints and special-effect
tones specifically designed for gray or white hair. Newest for
gray hair are the highlighting, conditioner-fortified shades of

gray ranging from steel, smoke, slate, and many other dark tones to pearl, platinum, and silver. Some are temporary, some semipermanent (lasting a month or more, depending on your individual hair and its growth rate). Like the fine finish on beautiful silver, these special-for-gray shades buff and polish your hair, giving it an incredible play of light and shadow. Yellow discoloration in gray or white hair is a thing of the past, for the new products take care of that in an instant. Special effects with subtle high-fashion tints of mauve, pink, sapphire, apricot—to name a few—are fun, too, if you're a party girl. Caution, though: The trend is toward a natural, glowing, luminous gray or white, not a shock-shade.

One reason for letting hair go completely white—perhaps even rushing the process as "grayness" grows—is a new kind of flattery. Silvery strands framing the paling skin tones of later years have a most complimentary, softening effect. And, there are exciting new things you can do with your new shade of hair. Stunning hairdos are being designed just for the snowy and silvery heads, gracious in line, smoothly elegant in style. Your coif may be a brief, pert one, or a dramatic upsweep for long or short hair. There are special permanents for you, too, to add body if the hair is thinning or to make wide, curving waves—without tightness or frizz. One hair-care hint: As your hair grows whiter, it may tend to dryness, seem coarser in texture. To keep your tresses in shining shape, plan a cream rinse after each shampoo; protect your head from extreme heat (and sun) or cold; and brush, brush, brush!

Whether you're prematurely gray (or white), gray by the grace of time, or looking hesitantly ahead to gray, you'll find many ways, many products—all practical—to make you a more glorious gray. The difference between dowdy or mousy gray and shining, lovely gray is simply a matter of choosing the right preparations and the right styling.

Hairstyles for the mature woman with gray hair should be selected on the same basis as for any other age (see Chapter III). But with these exceptions: avoid severe, straight-line coifs that tend to accentuate age; choose soft-line, face-framing styles that are feminine and romantic looking; never wear a mannish or Italian-boy cut that puts all the emphasis on the face; and avoid hairdos with "down" lines that underscore deepening facial lines around the mouth and eyes. Study the styles in the picture section of this book. There are several suitable ones for the older woman that are smart, pretty, and flattering to the mature face.

CHAPTER XVII

The Art of the Haircut

Haircutting is no longer a question of length or thinning. It graduated from the barber shop when the first hacked-off "bob" of the twenties went out of fashion. And with it went clippers and ruler-straight chopping. In the not too far future, as a matter of fact, the very word "haircut" may be passé, for the basis of today's lovely coifs is not really a cutting, but a shaping. And the secret of the easy-to-keep hairdo is a master shaping job.

What, then, is a good haircut or shaping? One that is right for your hair and becoming to your head and face. Properly done, a good cut will conform to your head, follow the growth pattern of your hair, bring out and emphasize curl *if* curl is latent in your hair and desirable, never look "fresh-cut" or choppy, improve the hair condition by removing split ends and making it "airier," and frame your face so that it looks becoming even before it is set. Large order? Yes, but those are the elements you should look for when you are having your hair cut. There is artistry in snipping hair for a smart hairdo, and the wise woman will neither cut her own nor be careless about her appointments for regular trimming and shaping.

There are two schools of thought on the tools for achieving a good haircut: One says you must have your hair shaped or cut only with a razor—no matter the texture, the thickness, or the degree of waviness; the other says fine hair must only be shaped with scissors, medium with a razor or scissors, and coarse with a razor. The razor-only school will argue that you can make only a straight cut with scissors—adding, for example, "Did you ever try to curl a paint brush?" (which, of course, is cut straight across and can't be softly curled at all). We won't choose sides, because we have seen master-pieces of shaping and styling done both ways. Scissors, in the hands of a skilled hairdresser, can be made to perform with exquisite artistry. If you've confidence in your stylist, let him have his way, and don't force him to do something he isn't accustomed to doing. All well-schooled operators are agreed on these two points, however: Clippers are taboo, and hair should be cut when it is wet. Clippers are disastrous not be-cause hair grows out coarser (the circumference of the hair shaft remains the same), but because it will grow straight out, feel stubbly, and look ugly. Hair should be cut when wet for several very good reasons. There is less margin for error in cutting, because your stylist can see exactly the amount of hair he is handling. The hair is relaxed when wet and will clearly show direction of growth and any tendency to curl or wave—which gives the stylist his clue for direction of cut. He can also see natural parting areas and cowlicks, if any.

Haircutting is undeniably an art, and, as with most arts, there are many techniques to it—a technique for each me-dium, each effect. In this art, the medium is the hair, the ef-fect, the style. And so, the "kindest cut" for you is not just any cut, but one that uses the technique suited to your particu-lar hair and your special style. Basically, there are six kinds of cuts. One of the six many be just right for your hair, or you may have a combination of two or more. See if you can decide which is best for you:

The taper cut: Also known as the "layer" or "leaf" or "petal" cut, this is used for shaping, thinning, and for giving extra bounce and body to extremely fine hair. There are many variations to this method, but most stylists prefer to cut the hair while it is wet, so its natural or permanent-wave inclination will show. Scissors are often used on fine or medium hair, a razor on coarse hair. (Thinning coarse hair is done this way—gone are most of those old-fashioned pruning shears with the teeth in them—and for very coarse hair the taper will be as much as a whole inch.) First step of this and every cut is sectioning—dividing the hair into sections for easy workability. Then, as he works, the stylist divides the section into strands. In tapering, the strand is drawn straight out from the head and held between the fingers at about a 45-degree angle. Then the strand is cut with a slithering movement of the scissors (or razor) so that ends are tapered. This slither cutting may be done on the top of the strand or underneath the strand, depending on the style, the hair, and the section of the head. (On the top layer, for example, the tapering is done underneath if a smooth contour is wanted; hair lies flat, no ends showing.)

The back-comb cut: Many taper cuts are done with back-combing used in the cut. This shapes the hair and removes the bulk, an important part of haircutting, for lighter masses of hair will curl more, lie better, be more easily controlled than hair that is weighted down with excess bulk. Hair is sectioned, as for the usual tapering, and the stylist works on each section, layer after layer. He holds the strand of hair (usually about one to two inches wide) straight out from the head, and brings the comb down the strand toward the scalp in three ruffing movements, until the comb is as close to the scalp as possible. This brings all the short hairs out of the strand. The smooth portion of the hair that is still remaining in the hand is cut with the scissors or razor. This leaves the ends nicely tapered, so that they blend together well, and still does not take out too much body. In this cut, as with other forms of taper cuts, the first section cut is used as a guide for length of the next layers.

The sculpture cut: This is a cut that follows the natural curl of the hair. Usually it needs no setting after the cut— just pushing into place with the fingers will hold the wave. This sort of cut is best on coarse hair, but it can be used by a skillful stylist on just about all but very fine or limp hair. Sectioning before the cut is done following the hair's natural tendencies, starting with the natural part. The wet hair is first worked and combed from all angles so that the stylist can determine the hair's natural movement. The stylist most often uses a razor for this cut, cutting in layers, but cutting to the natural curl of the hair. The strand of hair is held away from the scalp, the ends caught with the comb, and the shaping done with short, quick strokes of the razor. The stylist starts at the nape, thinning and shortening. Next, side hair is shaped and blended with the nape movement, then crown and top hair, so that all is molded together, sculptured to the head, in layers tapered all around.

The intra-curl cut: This cutting technique is the invention of the great stylist-consultant, Mme. Marguerite Buck. The idea here is to make the cut *into* the curl so it is never broken and each layer will blend perfectly with the next, fitting the head closely. Hair is cut section by section, starting from the sides (this way, the length of the back will be made to conform with the length most becoming to the front). The stylist takes the strand of wet hair between thumb and finger, slides his fingers down to about a half inch below the desired hair length. Now the hair is a flat ribbon. He relaxes the strand by moving his hand toward the head, then twists his wrist (not the strand) until the hair breaks in a circle. This shows the curve (natural or permanent wave) of the hair. He back-combs the strand to the ridge of the curve, pushes back short hairs. The scissors are placed horizontally on the ridge, beneath the back-combed hairs. On very coarse hair a razor will be used for tapering here, but the cut will still follow the curve's ridge.

The blunt cut: This cut—a straight-across stroke of the scissors on each strand—is used on very thin hair, to produce more body. It has also been used more recently on too wavy hair to encourage a smoother look. Hair is sectioned off as with other cuts. Usually the stylist works from the side to the back, working in layers. He picks up a strand and holds it out from the scalp, below the desired length. The scissors are used in quick, short strokes to make this blunt cut. The line of the first cut is followed around the back, usually graduating to longer length in the back. In the back, the blunt stroke is most often used only on the end hair; the layers just above are tapered to blend in with the ends. Hair on top is cut with the blunt stroke. Sometimes, as a softening variation of the cut, the strand of hair is twisted and then cut, producing less blunt, more easily blended ends.

The swing cut: This is a variation of the blunt cut. It starts with a blunt cut, but the usual straight edge is eliminated by a swinging stroke of the scissors. This is also good for fine or thin hair. Hair is sectioned as usual, and cutting usually begins at the side. Frequently, hair at the side, which is thinner, may get a straight blunt cut, with this variation used at the back. The strand of hair is held between the fingers, and the ends are flipped up. The cutting action here is a back-and-forth one—a whittle, actually, with the wrist swinging as the scissors cut. This produces an irregular blunt edge, and, when it is done in graduated layers, no rigid breaks will show. The top may be cut with blunt strokes, with ends evened off with this swing cut, using the swinging wrist action. Lengths will graduate from front to crown, but, with this whittle technique, the completed cut will have a good contour molding, no layer-on-layer look.

Can a haircut *make* hair curl? If the hair is actually straight, with no trace of a wave, the answer is a resounding "no." Various "curl-cuts" have been advertised with firm claims (never a guarantee) that this cut will make your hair curl. None has ever yet been devised. Several years ago, a hitherto unknown stylist in Manhattan soared into the limelight with a way of cutting the hair which produced humps-and-bumps that gave the hair a wavy look. It was done by actually shaving quarter-inch strips of the scalp in a pattern so that the remaining hair "humped" over the shaved areas to create the illusion of waves. The stylist enjoyed only brief fame—about as long as it took the first clients' hair to grow out. So-called "heat" cuts that claim curling properties can only produce temporary body in hair—and actually excessive heat can dry out scalp and hair.

So don't abandon your own perfectly good hairdresser for any wildly advertised curl-cut technician. Perfectly straight hair cannot be made to curl by cutting, and reason should tell you so, for the texture and curl disposition of your hair are with you from birth.

How often should you get your hair cut? The average woman's hair grows approximately a half inch in a month's time. And that half inch needs recutting because it takes just about that much on the average head to make the hair weighty and shapeless and to drag down a good setting. Once-a-month appointments are worth every penny you can afford for a good shaping, since you'll find that it all evens out in the end, when you do not have to have your hair set quite so often. And if, like most women today, you find time is worth money, too, then you'll really be ahead of the game, budgetwise. This once a month, of course, may stretch to six or eight weeks for some, may be as frequent as biweekly for others—all depending on how fast or how slowly your hair grows and whether yours is a brief or long hairdo. In any event, don't postpone your regular dates for shaping and trimming—they're the cornerstone of your well-groomed hairdo.

THE ART OF THE PART

Gone is the day when a part was just something you had on the right side or the left side or down the middle. Now a part is planned, deliberated upon, and put exactly where it is for an exact purpose. It may be placed to change the illusion of a face shape—to add a curve or straighten one, broaden a face or slim it, add height or contour or width. Perhaps it's placed to do a favor for eyes—play them up, accentuate them if they're especially lovely, or cover a defect, bring them closer together or move them farther apart—by camouflage or illusion. Perhaps a part is placed to camouflage a cowlick. Or it may be that the part is pure style, the inspiration for and starting place of a chic coif.

Irregular parts are fashion news at times, but they are also smart ways to beat cowlicks at the hairline. Making a part work with—not against—a back cowlick is a clever accomplishment of many hairdressers, with the hair arranged to swirl around the part in curving or waving lines as an integral part of the hairdo.

A part around the crown, with the hair swept smoothly to one side, across the brow, is a good shapemaker for the too square or too oblong face. A low side part can be the solution to many a face-shape problem—the oblong face, the narrow-brow pear-shape face, and more. It can also add height to the face or hide a specially bad cowlick.

A center part can be a boon or a bane. Use it to play up perfect features or an oval face. Use it also to bring in too wide-apart eyes. Avoid it if your face is round or markedly oblong or if eyes are too close together.

Diagonal parts, in conjunction with a full bang or a diagonal bandeau of hair can help disguise a brow that's too low. And, if you've a pretty profile, you can play it up with a profile part—one made directly across the crown, from ear to ear, and perhaps with added height at the back crown and back fullness to accentuate further the perfect profile.

CHAPTER XVIII

Handling and Styling Long Hair

If you're one of the many who wear their hair long, you should know the very special ways of caring for it—and the many ways in which it can be styled. Your reasons for never having your hair cut may be professional ones (many dancers and actresses feel that long hair is a necessity), or very personal ones (your husband or beau wouldn't hear of your cutting those long, romantic tresses). Whatever your reason for preferring long hair, don't fall into the booby trap of feeling that it's easier to handle, saves money and time at the hairdresser, or, worse yet, that it's the only way you can wear your hair.

Long hair need not be old-fashioned-looking. There are up-to-date ways to drape long locks, to swirl them, twirl them, pin them in practically limitless ways. (See some ways and techniques at the end of this chapter.) And long hair, to be truly an asset, must be more than flattering to your face and your stature; it should be a thing of beauty in and of itself, for it's a special feature in a predominantly short-hair fashion world, and it's an attention-getter. Why keep it long if it's not for the sheer beauty of it, the radiance of the silken length of it? If it's to be just that, then more than any other kind, long hair must be cared for tenderly, groomed to look and behave like satin.

Cleanliness comes first, for who can admire long dirty hair, long stringy hair, long dusty hair? All the basics apply to you with long hair (see Chapter VIII), plus some special extras. Extra length means extra time allotted for shampooing: Every inch should be conscientiously cleansed, from scalp to ends. If your hair is more oily than average, that may mean you should have three latherings rather than the usual two. Your hair, like any other, should be washed as often as washing is needed; if that means, in your case, twice weekly sessions, allow for them in your schedule (or seriously consider some cutting). Choice of shampoo is especially crucial for you, since your hair must always be kept in optimum condition.

Knots and tangles can pose a problem at shampoo time, for wet hair tends to tangle far more easily than dry. Your shampoo technique can prevent some of this postshampoo trouble. Working your fingers under the hair, close to the scalp, and moving them outward and fanning them from there, helps to separate the strands, keep them from matting. Then, for postshampoo combing, use a very strong comb with long, widely spaced teeth. Comb the ends first, grasping the hair a little way up from the ends. Then comb through a little higher and on up until you are combing from the scalp. No impatient pulling and yanking, please—comb gently, carefully, patiently.

You may think that long hair doesn't require setting. Why, you ask yourself, when it's simply going to be wrapped and pinned? The reason: not, as with short hair, for curl specifically, but for wave, body, and direction—to give the hair lift, mass, and guide-ability. So, if you'd have an attractive, manageable, long-hair style, you must set your locks. If your hair is fine, choose medium-size rollers; coarser hair requires the larger ones. If your hair tends to be dry and brittle at the ends, use endpapers or lamb's wool when setting clip curls (good, too, for the ends in the roller setting).

Unless you've hours to devote to drying your hair, you'll find a home dryer—one with an extra-roomy hood—an invaluable speed-up. A trial or two will tell you just how long your hair takes to dry thoroughly (a matter of both length and porosity); after that, it's simply a matter of setting a household timer.

Silkeners and smoothers are what make your long hair lovely and keep it that way. There's no general rule for what kind or how much, for they're geared to your hair, its texture, its own special needs. Buy the kind that's right for you, follow the directions, and use faithfully. Whatever your hair type, however, daily brushing is of utmost importance for distributing the natural oils the length of the long hair strands. That goes for oily hair too; undistributed oils tend to pool on and near the scalp and can promote dandruff. The time-honored method is best for you: head hanging forward, brushing in long strokes from the nape line up, forward to the forehead (reason: oil glands are usually more numerous toward the back).

Such after-shampoo aids as cream rinses and spray conditioners will be helpful if your hair tends to dryness. Extra-dry ends will benefit with a bit of hairdressing applied on ends only while the hair is still damp, just before setting. If your hair tends to dryness all over, you'll be wise to take preventive, protective measures—for correction of damage can be, for long hair, a tedious procedure. Protect your tresses from the elements' drying effects with sun hats, sun- and humidity-resistant sprays (sprayed very, very sparingly). And be specially careful in coloring or lightening or in choosing the colorist who does this for you. For any length of hair this is true, but for long hair, repairing mistakes in coloring is an expensive, time-consuming problem.

Keeping in trim is a must whether your hair is four inches

or four feet long. Yes, you should hie yourself to the hair-dresser for professional shaping at least every two months, and not just because your bangs or cheek curls have grown too long. All of your hair needs periodic trimming—even if it's only a tenth of an inch. This is necessary first, to remove any split or broken ends; second, because hair often grows at different rates on different parts of the head and evening avoids a choppy look that could easily spoil the line of your coif.

Split ends, of course, are the nemesis of any long-hair do, making it strawlike and shaggy where it should be silken and smooth. And hair that breaks off at the halfway point can be worst of all. Again, prevention of the problem is the key. Avoid teasing. If you need lift in your hairdo, try to confine very gentle back-combing to the better-lubricated back-of-the-crown area where most oil glands are concentrated. Select setting tools with extra care. Choose fine-quality clips that grip the hair without pinching and have no jagged, raw edges to tear hair. If you prefer brush rollers, be sure to choose either the natural-bristle kind or those whose nylon bristles are soft and rounded on the ends. And do try to avoid sleeping on clips or rollers.

Creating a coif for long hair takes imagination—plus pa-tience. Below you will find some ways for twisting and folding and arranging long locks. There are aids at your hair-care and cosmetics counters that can help to make your coif-creations more professional-looking. There are nearly in-visible nets that slip over the compact arrangements of buns, chignons, Psyche knots. There are combs and many other devices that are functional as well as ornamental, playing a part in the design of the hairdo. And there are preshaped mesh foundations to aid you in shaping rolls, buns, and such.

If your hair is the superfine kind, you may want to consider, strictly for body-building, a soft underperm (also known as a body permanent).

One final hint, especially for brunettes: Many of the styles you choose will be updos, dos that sweep the hair romantically up from the back of the neck so that your nape line is bared for all to see. If yours is less than ideal, do consider the possibility of permanent correction by way of professional electrolysis.

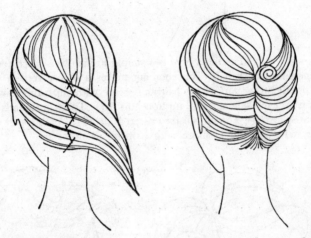

CLASSIC FRENCH ROLL—Different from the flatter French twist, this is a rounded put-up. Brush hair all to one side first and insert crisscross row of bobby pins as shown. Wrap hair back over pinned section, rolling ends smoothly inside. Fasten with hairpins.

FRENCH TWIST—The basis here is a simple French twist used for short or medium-length hair. Top combing makes a newer version of this classic. Begin by parting top hair and secure with clips. Lift lower section from each side and pull up to center back. Twist; tuck ends under in flat seam (see French roll for crisscross detail). Comb top smoothly over twist and pin in place with hairpins as necessary.

TOPKNOT COIL—Start with two ponytails anchored with coated-elastic bands as shown. Divide top tail in two. Coil one section to right, one to left. Pin ends under. Roll ends of lower tail under and fan out to meet coils. Tuck in and pin all ends securely, invisibly.

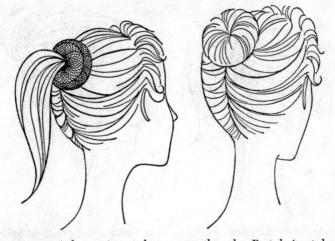

CARTWHEEL—A hoop ring makes a smoother do. Part hair at back; make ponytail of top half. Fold bottom half in French twist. Insert ponytail through center of ring; wrap hair around smoothly; fasten with pins.

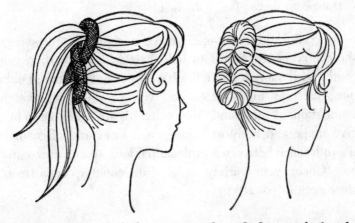

FIGURE EIGHT—Long locks here use a ready-made figure-eight foundation. Separate hair at back in two sections. Anchor each with coated-elastic band. Insert each tress through open part of foundation. Secure base with bobby pins. Cover base with hair, fanning each tress out to cover its half. Smooth and pin in place with hairpins.

PSYCHE KNOT—Simplest of all the classic twists is this pretty little knot. Pull hair back and up and fasten with coated band in ponytail style. Bend tail up; secure with a barrette above elastic. Wind hair around to cover and pin with "invisible" hairpins.

Drawings by Jo Lowrey.
© Dell Publishing Co., Inc., 1961, 1963.

NOTE: For these pin-ups, you've a choice of fastenings: the coated-elastic bands to hold hair without tearing; grip combs with many teeth in flexible strips of all lengths; bobby pins; hairpins in all sizes and colors. Many lightweight foundations of mesh and other materials are available to help give shape and body to home-grown locks and often make the difference between a professional look and an amateurish one. Check your variety store, drug counter, department-store notions counters.

CHAPTER XIX

Finishing Tricks with Hair Ornaments

Glitter and froufrou, jewels and baubles, everything from simple little flat bows to elaborate tiaras abound on the counters wherever hairdoing accessories are sold. The prettiest hairstyle in the world can often be that much more exciting and lovely with a little "top dressing." And for the party-bound coif, a touch of added glamour, a bit of fun, a dash of sparkle is almost a fashionable "must."

Hair ornaments may be bought or made by your own hands at home. There's an etiquette to wearing them too. Jewels, sequinned and glittery ornaments are strictly "after-five" dressing. For daytime—at the office, at school—the flat bow, tailored headband, or simple gold barrette is acceptable. Artificial or real flowers are best for special-occasion evening wear—with a few exceptions: at the beach, for outdoor afternoon parties, patio or terrace luncheons. Feathers, tiny plumes, circlets of gold leaves—these also belong in the dressier, after-five realm.

Here is a list of the kinds of hair ornaments you will find available when you shop for accessories.

Hairbands—of grosgrain, velvet, moire, satin, or embroidered ribbon. These have tiny elastic bands at the back to hide under your hairdo, and they may be just a plain band or a band with a flat bow at center front. Stretch jersey,

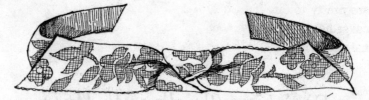

chiffon, and nylon-net bands are wider and come in every conceivable color to match almost any wardrobe. These are pretty as well as practical for the active sportswoman.

Hair clips—of plastic, in narrow and wide widths, are like bicycle-spring clips and partially circle the head to anchor a hairdo that goes straight back from the brow. Some varieties have little plastic grip teeth to insure secure holding. These are made in every color from plain white and clear to mottled, fake tortoise shell. Some kinds are covered with ribbon (often velvet) and have flat bows at center or side. Others have plastic or other artificial flowers glued to them. These are pretty to circle a topknot or a chignon, often serving to cover hairpins or bobby pins used in anchoring chignons or hairpieces.

Hair bows—of every kind of material: ribbons, plastic, leather, fake and real fur, mock alligator or lizard as well as the real thing, patent leather, horsehair, nylon net, stiff veiling material. Bows may be small, tailored, and flat and anchored to hair-setting clips, pronged barrettes, or tiny combs. They may be big and floppy to perch, almost hatlike, atop your hairdo or finish off the back of a back-interest coif. Ponytail bows come with elastic bands coated with silk or nylon thread. Very tiny velvet or satin bows on hair clips can camouflage a pin-curl setting when used in place of regular hair-setting clips, with the pretty result a headful of bows instead of bristling metallic clips.

Combs—in a variety of sizes are topped with jewels of all

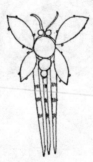

kinds for tucking here and there into a hairdo as well as for serving the purpose of securing French twists, rolls, chignons, hairpieces. These decorative combs may be all glittery—as pretty as any costume jewelry you own—or they may have flowers, bows, butterflies of net or sequins, gold leaves, or gilt posies.

Barrettes—of brushed gold, silver, seed pearls, rhinestones, colored plastic, or real or fake tortoise shell hold strands of hair in place, add a simple finish to a simple do, or accent with glitter a more complicated coif. Used singly, in pairs, or, in the case of very tiny ones, dotted throughout a hairdo, the barrette is functional as well as decorative.

Tiaras and coronets—traditionally of rhinestones, but varied now with airy, wired, seed-pearl construction, are worn for highly formal evening affairs. Proms and formal dances are logical occasions for elaborate up-dos topped with a jeweled circlet, a tiara, or a tiny infanta crown of glitter. A cluster of wee ostrich plumes fixed with a jeweled diadem is another pretty conceit for such affairs.

Flowers—on clips, bands, and combs to tuck in a clump

or a spray or dotted individually throughout a hairdo are pretty dress-ups for summer. Artificial daisies, a cluster of forget-me-nots, a big, floppy silk rose—these are a few of the suitable flowers that can put a finishing touch on your coif.

If you're in a hurry, if you've no time to shop for that little bit of top dressing, here are some impromptu things you can do:

Raid your own costume-jewelry cache to find sparkly pins to tuck into a romantic hairdo.

Clip an odd earring (who doesn't own at least one that's lost its mate?) right into your hair or onto a strong bobby pin to tuck into a cluster of curls or at the curve of a wide guiche.

Try a bangly choker as a back-on-the-head headband.

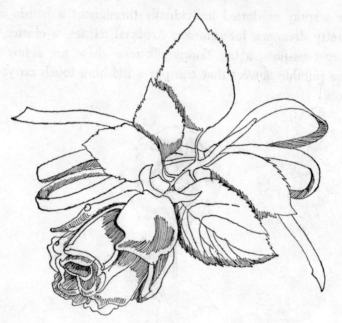

Deck a ribbon-covered plastic hair clipband with a favorite glittery broach or clip.

Plop a cluster of fake or in-season real flowers right in the center top of your hairdo, fastening it with springy bobby pins.

Use a wide jewel-paved bracelet as a small crown atop an up-do or use the same bracelet to circle a low-fastened chignon.

And, if you're an artist at bow-tying and have an eye for pretty ribbons, you might try making some of these:

Cockade: Use 1-inch or 1½-inch ribbon, plaid, plain, or checked, about a yard. Cover a small button with the ribbon. Then fold remaining ribbon into tiny box pleats. Tack pleats in place and gather around the button, fastening with close stitches behind the button so that the result looks like a

rosette. Tack to a barrette or hair-setting clip as is and tuck in hair, or add short ribbon streamers tacked to back of the cockade. In heavy satin ribbon, this can be centered with a tiny jeweled pin for dressier hairdos.

Satin fringe: Use 2-inch-wide satin ribbon. Make a flat, tailored bow (like Mary Jane shoe bows or dancing-pump bows) with the "knot" a separate flat piece whipstitched on the under side. Tack two short streamers to back of bow, leaving one end slightly longer than the other. Fringe the silk ends to a depth of about a half inch. Sew bow to small comb or setting clip. Wear this one high on the side of a

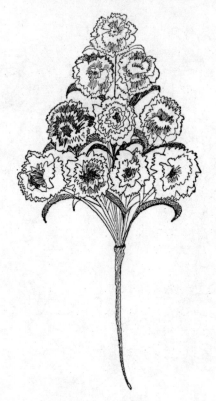

smooth, medium-length bob with ends flipped out or under.

Shoestring bow: Use cord trimming, colored yarn, the narrowest grosgrain ribbon, or make your own "string" by making cording from fabric to match a favorite dress. Form loopy bow with tails as long as you wish or tie several of the strings into one bow to form a "spaghetti" bow. Tack to a clip and tuck at back or side of your hairdo. These are pretty in black but also fun in multicolor.

Pompon: Use two different shades of a quarter-inch ribbon—grosgrain, satin, or velvet—and, working with the two colors together, form into a circle of loops, catching each loop with needle and thread in center as it is formed. Fasten

Drawings in this chapter by Richard Giglio.
© Dell Publishing Co., Inc., 1962.

to clip at back. Another way: make pompon with colored yarn, using two or three shades and securing with yarn wound around center.

Bands: Using an inexpensive narrow plastic hairband-clip, decorate it quickly and easily as you will. Use one of the adhesives available in the dime store for glueing fabric (without stains or show-through) and cover the plastic base with, say, gingham or calico to match a dress of the same material. Cover with ribbons of your choice and add (with the same adhesive) a row of tiny matching bows, a big loop-bow at one side, tiny artificial flowers, small seashells, or rhinestones and glitter as you wish. This way you'll have custom headbands you've designed yourself for a more co-ordinated look with your own clothes.

Giant bows: Use wide moire taffeta, velvet, satin ribbon, narrow-width stiff veiling, white eyelet embroidery, or lace. Tie into puffy bow. Slip bobby pin or clip into knot to hold. To keep bow full at sides and in place atop your coif, tack tiny clips at each loop end, to anchor in hair.

These are but a few ideas to springboard you to creative ones of your own. The more you experiment, the more inventive you'll discover that you are and the prettier and more individual will be your "top dressing."

CHAPTER XX

Some Professional Secrets

Masters of the hairstyling art have many little tricks they've invented to achieve better settings and to make the hairdos they've created last longer, stay prettier. Here are some tips gleaned for your guidance in keeping your own coif salon-perfect between appointments with your hairdresser or for making your home hairdoing more professional:

Prevent brush-out "breaks" in smooth, no-part hairdos this way: stagger the sections slightly as you roll hair in setting it; use imperfect or zigzag sectionings made with the point of a rattail comb. And, when fastening a roller, clip it to the next one in line—using one clip to hold two rollers in place.

If regular setting lotions do not seem to provide enough body for your hairdo, take a tip from many of the professionals who use one or more of these: milk, sugar water, egg whites, beer. Beer is allowed to go flat first, then used as is or mixed half-and-half with your favorite setting lotion. Fresh egg whites are mixed with water in the proportion of two parts water to one part egg white and whipped thoroughly. The mixture is applied section by section as you set your hair. Sugar is mixed—one teaspoonful to one eight-ounce cup of water (lukewarm)—with water until dissolved. Used as a setting lotion, it has a stiffening effect on the hair and seems to increase body and manageability. If one teaspoonful is not effective, increase to two teaspoonfuls in a cup of water. Milk is the dry, powdered variety, reconstituted with water according to package directions. It may then be transferred to a pump-dispenser or plastic-applicator bottle and applied as a setting lotion after hair has been towel-dried. Some of these homemade setting aids leave a film on the hair and make for a dulling effect. The answer lies in extremely vigorous brush-out, which will remove the solution's dulling residue without destroying the firming effect provided.

A bouffant or high-style hairdo may be preserved by simply placing clips in strategic hairline details—in the ridges of deep waves, across wide guiches or cheek curls, for instance—and then winding toilet tissue all around your hairdo, fastening the final strip with a clip. Then place a net over all before going to sleep on your coif-cocoon.

Coarse hair with a mind of its willful own can be disciplined in the setting as well as with conditioners, sprays, other taming preparations. The professional added advice: Wrap pin-curled strands, not just rolled ones, in endpapers. And try longer drying time at lower temperatures.

Professionals and home hair-doers who are perfectionists do this to achieve fine settings and smooth brush-outs: Instead of clips, fasten rollers with picks (the plastic kind available wherever hairdo accessories are sold) that leave no lines and won't rock or jar the roll off center.

Is there one strand that simply won't behave when you brush out your set? Back-comb or back-brush it underneath, and then smooth it in place, topside, with a brush or fine-tooth comb.

When a brush-out is complete, then lightly spray to hold the hairdo in place, and do it as the stylists do: Spray the entire head (quickly, moving around and around the head and holding the spray ten-to-twelve inches from the hair), a little more at the nape and the hairline. Then spread your fingers and cup your hairdo gently with them to hold while the spray dries—just a few seconds. For an extra-fine mist, net the hairdo first (use a fine nylon net like maline) and spray through the net.

The care and keeping of the guiche—that sleek curl drawn out to cheek or jawbone—has inspired many a resourceful innovation. Try setting its flat, fashionable arc with a strip of cellophane placed lightly across it (a good tip for bangs settings too!). To keep it close to the face at the very tip, try a drop of surgical adhesive (in a tube at your drugstore) or a dot of clear nail polish under the tip.

For fine hair settings that tend to droop like wilted blossoms a day after you've been to the hairdresser, try two small fluffs of wool or cotton instead of endpapers when putting up hair at night.

Never dip-comb or pour on setting solutions. Instead, keep your favorite solution in an atomizer or pump-dispenser bottle, and apply to a strand at a time, not the whole head.

For puffy bangs that tend to collapse, spray with a little setting lotion or hair spray, then place a large roll of cotton under bangs, combing smoothly over roll and clip cotton to temples at each side. Tuck ends of bangs under the roll. This is a good trick for a sagging page-boy do, with a much larger roll of cotton, of course.

Use two brushes, as the best stylists do when brushing and stimulating scalp before a shampoo—it's quicker, and oil is distributed faster, surface dirt removed more quickly.

Never stretch hair when it's wet. Wind rollers loosely for smooth, soft dos; don't pull or stretch the damp tress.

Use as few clips and pins as possible. One pin curl, properly wound, need have but one small clip to hold it. Hair which is porous, overbleached, excessively dry from overexposure, will tend to have imprints of the clips which are placed like X's across curls. This will result in "fishhooks" in the brush-out (see Chapter VI for details on improving or perfecting your setting technique). Many hair stylists feel that the home setting of hair fails because hairdos are over-set, with far too many implements used. The smooth, simple hairdos currently in fashion for daytime wear are set with very large rollers, and very few of those, with the addition of a few clip curls at nape and cheek lines. The fewer the rollers and clips, the smoother will be the resultant coif, say the experts.

CHAPTER XXI

Old Wives' Tales

We've all heard them—and from young wives as well as old. Some are ancient superstitions. Some are simply false. Others have been, in the course of time and scientific advance, disproved. And in a few, there's an element of truth. "Cutting the hair," goes one old tale, "will make it grow faster." No, it will not. It won't affect your hair's growth rate in the slightest. That depends on two things: your heredity and your health. Your hair, as we have said, will grow, if you're one of the average, at the rate of about one half inch per month. Some women's will grow as much as an inch; others, perhaps, about a quarter of an inch. There is no truth either in that spooky legend that hair and nails grow after death. As soon as blood circulation stops, all body processes cease to function, and, therefore, hair stops growing. With death, the pores of the body close quickly and shrink away from the hair shaft, thus giving the illusion of very slight growth for the moment. Shaving or close clipping of the hair of the head or hair on other parts of the body does not encourage growth, nor coarsen hair, as the tale goes. What it does do is make hair feel stubbly as it grows out again, because it is short and growing at nearly right angles to the skin or scalp.

Many a mother has coaxed her little girl with this one: "Eat your carrots—they'll make your hair curl." Let's call that one a white lie, since the carrots are chock-full of vitamin A and unquestionably nutritional. Neither carrots, butter, cream nor any other food will make hair wave. Hair will only be as curly as heredity factors—or a permanent wave—will make it.

"Her hair turned white—overnight!" Possible? All the visible hair on the lady's head? Short of an all-night bleaching session, no. But there are cases on record in which sudden trauma, physical or emotional, has effected a halt in the activity of the scalp's pigment-making cells. Thus new growth has been colorless, or white; all of which takes growth time to be visible, and no immediately apparent next morning change could be possible.

Then there are the old wives' tales about permanents. "They won't 'take' if . . ." If you're pregnant, or are menstruating, or have had novocaine at the dentist's or anaesthesia in the hospital—to name a few of the "ifs." An internal upset can affect future growth and hair condition, but not the hair that's being waved. Excessive dryness of the hair or excessive oiliness may, however, require, at certain times, a preconditioning of the hair for the most successful permanents.

"Your hair falls out after you've had a baby." Not true any more than that old saw, "For every child, a tooth is lost." Hormonal changes within the body during pregnancy, the tremendous exertion of the body in giving birth may account for some women's experiencing a short period after delivery during which hair may seem limp and a certain amount of "fall-out" ensues. The average woman does not have this problem; for the few who do: Courage—the condition is only temporary until your system returns to normal.

Shampooing is another popular subject. "Don't wash your hair during 'that time of the month'" (meaning, your menstrual period). And, "Mustn't shampoo too often—bad for the hair." The latter is just plain wrong; the cleaner your hair, the better. If you use the right shampoo for your hair type, rinse thoroughly, and dry just as thoroughly, you may wash your hair as often as you wish without damaging it. Frequent washing neither dries out the scalp, stunts hair growth, produces baldness, nor increases dandruff. As for the former statement—that originated in the era before well-heated, well-insulated homes, when baths, too, were considered injurious at this time. Today we know better. You wouldn't, of course, go out in a chill autumn breeze while your hair's wet, then, or at any other time.

"Baldness is a sign of unusual mental powers and, in men, a sign of virility." Many, but not all intellectuals are bald. The truth is that, as a type, many "brainy" people tend to be nervous and high-strung, with a tendency toward derangements of the glandular system. Hence their weakened health produces weak hair or no hair.

"Children's hair is weaker and more delicate than adults." True, it is indeed of a finer texture, in general, when the child is very young, but it is much more stubborn as the pattern of growth evolves.

"Singeing will correct a split-ends condition." Singeing will burn off existing split ends but will not correct or prevent the production of new ones. In addition, singeing tends to dry out hair ends and induce brittleness. Good conditioning, trimming split ends with razor or scissors—these are the modern methods for clearing up this problem.

"Too many cocktails spoil the wave." Moderate imbibing cannot ruin hairdo or permanent. But excess alcohol in the system can certainly impair your health—and good health is a prerequisite to a good head of hair and a beautiful hairdo.

"Typical redhead—what a temper!" Her disposition might indeed be inflammable, but don't blame her flame-colored hair. Sheer coincidence, that. This is a myth that originated in ancient England, where an aversion to the red-haired Danish invaders prevailed. Redheads were held in contempt and regarded as cruel-tempered people. Normally even-tempered school children with red hair often rebel explosively at nicknames like "Red" or "Carrottop" or "Brick top," and this fact has undoubtedly helped to perpetuate the myth. "Gentlemen prefer blondes," "Brunettes are sultry or sullen"—just as untrue, for the color of the hair is no clue to the temperament of the individual.

"I was so scared," she reports after the horror movie, "that my hair stood on end." She thinks she's using a figure of speech; strangely enough, it may have been true. Extreme fright can cause blood-vessel and muscle reactions near the surface of the skin—which can indeed, through contraction, cause the area around each hair to hold the hair up stiffly. On our arms or legs, we call the phenomenon "goose pimples."

Those are most of the old wives' tales you will hear from time to time. It's up to you to sort the fact from the fancy and help debunk some of the myths and superstitions.

Index